Lecture-Tutorials

For Introductory Astronomy

Fourth Edition

Edward E. Prather
University of Arizona

Gina Brissenden
University of Arizona

Colin S. Wallace
UNC Chapel Hill

Jeffrey P. Adams
Millersville University

with contributions by

Jack A. Dostal
Wake Forest University

Seth Hornstein
University of Colorado Boulder

Michael LoPresto
University of Michigan

Tim Chambers
University of Michigan

 Pearson

Content Management: Jeanne Zalesky, Deborah Harden
Content Production: Kristen Flathman, Shercian Kinosian, Bhavani Pushparaj
Product Management: Christopher Hess, Jessica Moro
Product Marketing: Candice Madden, Rosemary Morton
Rights and Permissions: Ben Ferrini, Angelica Aranas, Mariel Papauran

Please contact https://support.pearson.com/getsupport/s/ with any queries on this content

Cover Image Owner: VICTOR de SCHWANBERG/SCIENCE PHOTO LIBRARY/Getty Images

Inside Back Cover Image: NASA Galaxy images

Photos courtesy of: 113 University of California Observatories; 170 NASA; 163/173/178
Stocktrek Images, Inc./Alamy Stock Photo; 91/95 Peter Hermes Furian/Alamy Stock Photo;
121 CLAUS LUNAU/Science Source; 167 Robert Williams and the Hubble Deep Field Team
(STScI) and NASA; 185 Science Photo Library/Alamy Stock Photo

Text Courtesy of: 116 GOODY & WALKER, ATMOSPHERES, 1st Ed., © 1973. Reprinted
and electronically reproduced by permission of Pearson Education, Inc., Upper Saddle River,
New Jersey.

Instant Access Code
ISBN 10: 0-137-61964-2
ISBN 13: 978-0-137-61964-1

6 2022

Lecture-Tutorials
ISBN 10: 0-135-80702-6
ISBN 13: 978-0-135-80702-6

The Night Sky

Fundamentals of Astronomy

Nature of Light in Astronomy

Our Solar System

Stars, Galaxies, and Beyond

Instructor's Preface

Each year, over 250,000 students take introductory astronomy—hereafter referred to as Astro 101; the majority of these students are non-science majors. Most are taking Astro 101 to fulfill a university science requirement, and many approach science with some mix of fear and disinterest. The traditional approach to help students learn has been to emphasize creative and engaging lectures, taking full advantage of both demonstrations and awe-inspiring astronomical images. However, a growing body of evidence in astronomy and physics education research demonstrates that even the most popular and engaging lectures do not engender the depth of learning for which faculty appropriately aim. Rigorous research into student learning tells us that one critical factor missing from the traditional lecture-based classrooms is the ability to intellectually engage students in collaborative learning environments where they construct their own understanding while working through active-learning activities. This is best expressed in the mantra: "It's not what the teacher does that matters; rather it's what the students do that matters."

Lecture-Tutorials for Introductory Astronomy has been developed in response to the demand from astronomy instructors for easily implemented active-learning activities for integration into existing course structures. Rather than asking faculty—and students—to convert to an entirely new course structure, our approach in developing Lecture-Tutorials was to create classroom-ready materials to augment traditional lectures. Any of the activities in this manual can be inserted at the end of lecture presentations, and because of the education research program that led to the activities' development, we are confident in asserting that the activities will lead to deeper and more enduring student understanding of the concepts addressed.

Each Lecture-Tutorial presents a structured series of questions designed to help student confront and resolve conceptual and reasoning difficulties. Confronting difficulties often means answering questions incorrectly; this is expected. When this happens, the activities make use of additional questions or situated student debates designed to help a student understand where her or his reasoning went wrong and to develop a more thorough understanding as a result. Therefore, while completing the activities, students are encouraged to focus more on their reasoning and less on trying to guess an expected answer. The activities are meant to be completed by students working in pairs who "talk out" their answers and reasoning with each other to make their thinking explicit.

At the conclusion of each Lecture-Tutorial, instructors are encouraged to engage their class in a brief discussion about the particularly difficult concepts in the activity. The online Instructor's Guide[1] also provides "post-tutorial" questions that can be used to gauge the effectiveness of the Lecture-Tutorial before moving on to new material.

Unique to this fourth edition of Lecture-Tutorials for Introductory Astronomy are seven new activities focusing on topics not found in the third edition. These all-new activities were specifically chosen to fill gaps from the third edition regarding the most common topics taught in an Astro 101 course. As a result, there are now new activities that focus on more various topics. It's now possible to complement your instruction with the "Observing the Universe with Multiple Telescopes," "Observing the Invisible—Molecular Excitations and Synchrotron Radiation," "Formation of Planets in the Solar System," "Sizing Up the Planets," "Comparing the Surfaces of Planets," "Detecting Exoplanets with the Transit Method" and "Detecting Exoplanets with Gravitational Microlensing" Lecture-Tutorials. These new activities

---

[1]Instructors can go to http://www.pearsonhighered.com for an online Instructor's Guide that gives detailed information on classroom implementation as well as evidence of the efficacy of specific activities.

have been through the same rigorous development cycle that was used to create the highly successful activities of the first, second and third editions.

In addition, several changes have been made to your favorite activities from the previous editions of *Lecture-Tutorials.* Over the last several years, we have performed continuous and systematic research to uncover places where students struggle with the wording of questions or scenarios presented in the *Lecture-Tutorial* activities. As a result, many activities from the previous editions have been notably changed for the fourth edition. In particular, the diagrams, graphs, and artwork have been significantly improved to help students make hard-to-visualize and perceptually complex ideas more accessible and easier to comprehend.

Acknowledgments

Lecture-Tutorials for Introductory Astronomy was developed with generous support from the National Science Foundation (#0715517, #9952232, #9907755), the Jet Propulsion Laboratory's NASA Exoplanet Exploration Program, the Spitzer Education and Public Outreach Programs, Montana State University, the Conceptual Astronomy and Physics Education Research (CAPER) team, the University of Arizona, and the Center for Astronomy Education (CAE). Numerous individuals contributed to this project through critical assessment and the national field-testing of the materials. These individuals include Ingrid Balsa, Chija Skala Bauer, Erik Brogt, Tom Brown, Dave Bruning, Sébastien Cormier, Erin Dokter, Doug Duncan, Thomas Fleming, Beth Hufnagel, John Keller, Janet Landato, Ed Murphy, Erika Offerdahl, Larry Watson, Briana Ingermann, Julia Kamenetzky, Paul Robinson, Wayne Schlingman, and Molly Simon. Particularly noteworthy were the extensive reviews and suggestions provided by Rica Sirbaugh French, Dan Loranz, Janelle Bailey, Lauren Jones, Steve Shawl, and Alex Storrs, which continually kept us on our toes. We would like to acknowledge Molly Simon and Briana A. Ingermann for taking a leadership role on the development of one of more of the new activities. In addition, we must thank Nancy Whilton and Tema Goodwin, who helped us with day-to-day publication issues in previous editions and Deborah Harden, Shercian Kinosian and Bhavani Pushparaj for helping us on this new edition. Most importantly, we wish to express our appreciation to all of the students who patiently endured early versions of these tutorials and unselfishly provided extensive feedback.

Note to the Student

Welcome to the study of astronomy! You are about to embark on a grand study of the cosmos. To help you better understand the topics of your course, we have created this series of activities called *Lecture-Tutorials.* In each activity, you are asked a short series of questions that will require you to work in collaboration with your classmates to help you learn important and difficult concepts in astronomy. For every question in these activities, it is important that you write out a detailed answer. This is critical because you will certainly be using these materials to study for exams. It is also important because part of the learning process is being able to express complex ideas in writing.

We strongly encourage you to actively engage in completing these activities in collaboration with another student. The process of deciphering the questions and negotiating a common language to write your answers will help you understand the concepts more deeply. Specifically, the *Lecture-Tutorials* are designed to give you a starting point to think carefully and talk with others about concepts in astronomy. Above all, have fun exploring astronomy!

—Ed Prather, Gina Brissenden, Colin Wallace, and Jeff Adams

In this celestial sphere model, Earth is stationary and the stars are carried on a sphere that rotates about an axis that points at the North Star. In Figure 1 below, two stars, A and B, are each shown at four different positions (1, 2, 3, and 4) through which each star will pass during the course of one revolution of the celestial sphere. In addition, your location on Earth in the Northern Hemisphere is shown. Note that only the portion of the celestial sphere that is above the horizon is shown.

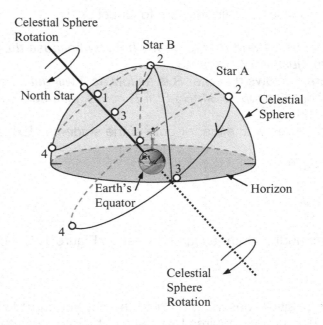

Figure 1

1) Is the horizon shown a real physical horizon or an imaginary plane that extends from your observing location on Earth out to the celestial sphere?

2) Can the observer shown see a star when it is located below the horizon? Why or why not?

3) Is either Star A or B ever in an unobservable position? If so, which position(s)?

4) When a star travels from a position below the observer's horizon to a position above the observer's horizon, is that star rising or setting?

5) When a star travels from a position above the observer's horizon to a position below the observer's horizon, is that star rising or setting?

---

6) Star A is just visible above your eastern horizon at Position 1. At which of the numbered positions is it just visible above your western horizon?

7) At which position(s), if any, does Star B rise and set?

8) Two students are discussing their answers to Question 7.

   Student 1: *Locations B1 and B3 are on my horizon because they are rising and setting just like A1 and A3.*

   Student 2: *Figure 1 shows that Star B is as low as it will get when it is just above the northern horizon at B4. So Star B never goes below the horizon.*

   Do you agree or disagree with either or both of the students? Explain your reasoning.

9) Label the directions north, south, east, and west on Figure 1. Check your answer with another group.

10) For each indicated position, describe where in the sky you must look to see the star at that time. Each description requires two pieces of information: the direction you must face (north, northeast, east, etc.) and how far above the horizon you must look (low, high, or directly overhead). If you cannot see the star, state that explicitly. The descriptions for four positions are given as examples.

   a) A1: *east, low*

   b) A2:

   c) A3:

   d) A4:

   e) North Star: *north, high*

   f) B1:

   g) B2: *directly overhead*

   h) B3: *northwest, high*

   i) B4:

   Check your answers with a nearby group and resolve any inconsistencies.

11) Does Star B ever set?

Part I: Looking North

For this activity, imagine you are the observer shown on Earth in the Northern Hemisphere and that the time is 6 P.M. Looking north, the sky will appear as shown in Figure 1. The positions and motions of the star in Figure 1 can be understood by imagining yourself as the observer at the center of the celestial sphere as shown in Figure 2. In the celestial sphere model, Earth is stationary and the stars are carried on a sphere that rotates about an axis that points at the North Star. Note that only the portion of the celestial sphere that is above your horizon is shown.

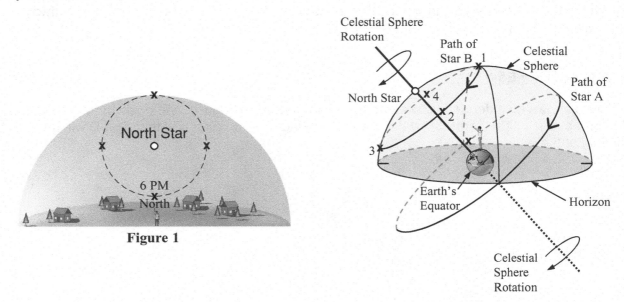

Figure 1

Figure 2

The **x**'s in both figures represent four of the positions through which Star B will pass during the course of one revolution of the celestial sphere. Ignore Star A until Question 6.

1) Note in Figure 1 that the position of Star B at 6 P.M. has been identified for you. Circle the numbered position (1, 2, 3, or 4) in <u>Figure 2</u> that corresponds to the identified location of Star B at 6 P.M. provided in Figure 1.

2) The rotation of the celestial sphere carries Star B around so that it returns to the same position at about 6 P.M. the next evening. Label each of the **x**'s in both figures with the approximate time at which Star B will arrive (e.g., the location you circled in Question 1 will be labeled "6 P.M.").

3) Using Figure 2, describe the direction you have to look to see Star B at 6 A.M.

4) The position directly overhead is called the **zenith**. Label the direction of the zenith on Figure 2.

5) In Figure 1, the path that Star B follows is shown with a dashed line. Draw a small arrowhead on the path to represent the direction Star B would be moving at the instant it is at each of the four locations marked with an **x**.

6) Imagine you could see Star B at noon. Fifteen minutes later, in what direction will Star B have moved? Explain your reasoning.

7) Using Figure 2, describe in words where you would look to see Star A when it is halfway between rising and setting.

Part II: Looking East

Figure 3 shows an extended view along the eastern horizon showing the positions of Stars A and B at 6 P.M. The arrow shown is provided to indicate the direction that Star B will be moving at 6 P.M.

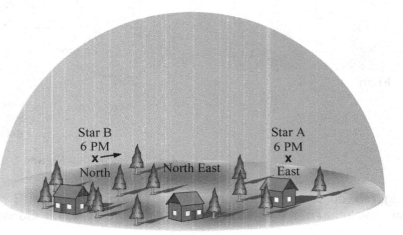

Figure 3

8) Recall that in Question 7, you found that Star A ends up high in the southern sky when it is halfway between rising and setting (and therefore never passes through your zenith). Draw a straight arrow at the **x** in the east in Figure 3 (the position of Star A at 6 P.M.) to indicate the direction Star A moves as it rises. Studying Figure 2 can also help clarify your answer.

9) Two students are discussing the direction of motion of a star rising directly in the east.

   Student 1: *Stars move east to west so any star rising directly in the east must be moving straight up so that it can later set in the west. If the arrow were angled, the star would not travel so that it would set in the west.*

   Student 2: *I disagree. From Figure 2, the path of Star A starts in the east at the horizon, and then it goes up and will later be high in the southern sky, and then it will set in the west. To do this it has to move toward the south as it rises so I drew my arrow angled up and to the right.*

   Do you agree or disagree with either or both of the students? Explain your reasoning.

10) Consider the student comment below.

Student: *The amount of time that all stars are above the horizon is 12 hours because it takes 12 hours for a star to rise in the east and then set in the west.*

Do you agree or disagree with the student? Explain your reasoning.

Consider the situation shown below in which the Sun and a group of constellations are shown at sunrise, Figure 4, and then shown again 8 hours later, Figure 5.

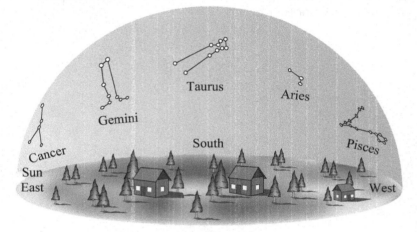

Figure 4

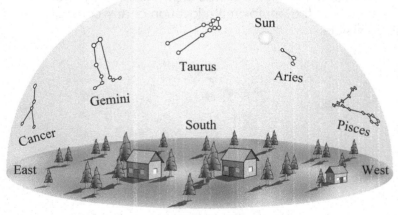

Figure 5

Motion

11) Consider the following debate between two students regarding the motion of the Sun and constellations shown in Figures 4 and 5.

Student 1: *We know the Sun rises in the east and moves through the southern part of the sky and then sets in the west. Eight hours after sunrise, it makes sense that the Sun will have moved from being on the eastern horizon near the constellation Cancer to being located high in the southwestern sky near the constellation Aries.*

Student 2: *You're forgetting that some stars and constellations also move from the east through the southern sky and to the west just like the Sun. So, the Sun will still be near Cancer eight hours later. So Figure 5 is drawn incorrectly. It should show that the constellations have all moved like the Sun, so Cancer would also be located high in the southwestern sky, with the Sun, eight hours later.*

Do you agree or disagree with either or both of the students? Explain your reasoning. Check your answers with another group.

12) In Question 11, we found that Figure 5 was drawn incorrectly. Redraw Figure 5 on the figure below by sketching the approximate location of any constellations from Figure 5 that would still be visible.

Part I: Monthly Differences

Figure 1 shows a Sun-centered, or heliocentric, perspective view of the Earth–Sun system indicating the direction of both the daily rotation of Earth about its own axis and its yearly orbit about the Sun. You are the observer shown in Figure 1, located on Earth in the Northern Hemisphere while facing south.

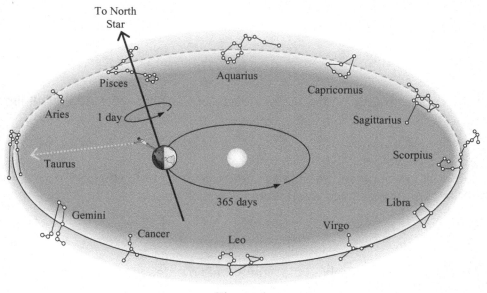

Figure 1

Figure 2 shows a horizon view of what you would see when facing south on this night at the same time as shown in Figure 1.

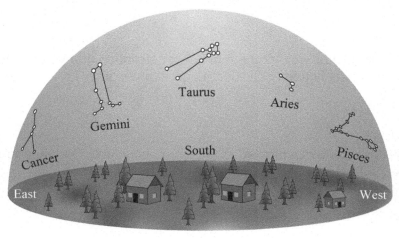

Figure 2

1) Which labeled constellation do you see highest in the southern sky?

2) For the time shown, which constellation is just to the east (i.e., to your left when you are facing south) and which constellation is just to the west (i.e., to your right when you are facing south) of the highest constellation at this instant?

east: west:

3) Noting that you are exactly on the opposite side of Earth from the Sun, what time is it?

4) In six hours, will the observer be able to see the Sun? If not, why not? If so, in what direction (north, south, east, or west) would you look to see the Sun?

5) Which constellation will be behind the Sun at the time described in Question 4?

6) When it is noon for the observer, which constellation will be behind the Sun?

7) One month later, Earth will have moved one-twelfth of the way around the Sun. You are again facing south while observing at midnight. Which constellation will now be highest in the southern sky?

8) Do you have to look east or west of the highest constellation that you see now to see the constellation that was highest one month ago at midnight?

9) Does the constellation that was highest in the sky at midnight a month ago now rise earlier or later than it rose last month? Explain your reasoning.

Part II: Daily Differences

Figure 3 shows the same Earth–Sun view as before and the bright star Betelgeuse, which is between Taurus and Gemini.

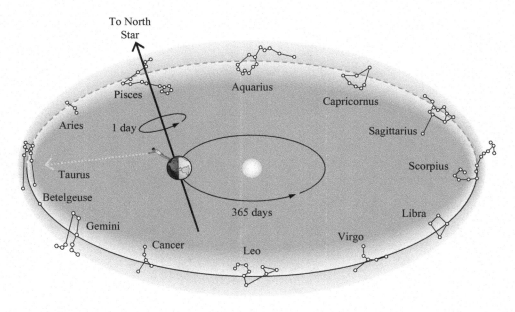

Figure 3

10) Imagine last night you saw the star Betelgeuse just starting to rise on your eastern horizon at 7:15 P.M. At 7:15 P.M. tonight, will Betelgeuse be above, below, or exactly on your eastern horizon?

11) Two students are discussing their answers to Question 10.

Student 1: *Earth makes one complete rotation about its axis each day so Betelgeuse will rise at the same time every night. It will therefore be exactly on the eastern horizon.*

Student 2: *I disagree. Recall that since Earth goes around the Sun, the constellation Taurus rises earlier each month and so it must rise a little bit earlier each night, too. Betelgeuse must do the same thing. Tonight it would rise a little before 7:15 and be above the eastern horizon by 7:15.*

Do you agree or disagree with either or both of the students? Explain your reasoning.

Part I: Solar Day

Figure 1 shows a top-down view of the Earth–Sun system. Arrows indicate the directions of the rotational and orbital motions of Earth. For the observer shown, the Sun is highest in the sky at noon.

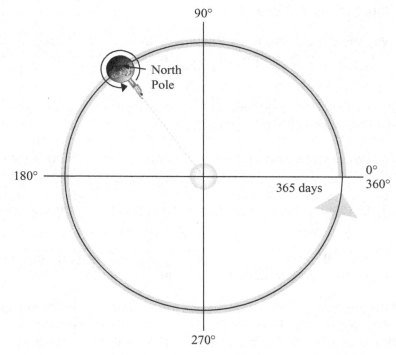

Figure 1

1) Earth orbits the Sun in a counterclockwise direction once every 365 days. Approximately how many degrees does Earth move along its orbit in one day?

2) As Earth orbits the Sun, it also rotates in a counterclockwise direction about its axis as shown in Figure 1. We define 24 hours as the time from when the Sun is highest in the sky one day to when it is highest in the sky the next day. How many degrees does Earth rotate about its axis in exactly 24 hours: 360°, slightly less than 360°, or slightly more than 360°?

3) How long does it take Earth to rotate exactly 360°: slightly less than 24 hours, 24 hours, or slightly more than 24 hours?

4) Two students are discussing their answers to Questions 2 and 3.

   Student 1: *Earth rotates about its axis once every 24 hours, and one rotation equals 360°.*

   Student 2: *I disagree. When Earth has gone around 360° it has also moved a small amount counterclockwise around the Sun, which means the Sun will not appear highest in the sky yet after a 360° rotation. Earth must spin a little bit more for the Sun to reach its highest point.*

   Do you agree or disagree with either or both of the students? Explain your reasoning.

Part II: Sidereal Day

We define a **solar day** as the time it takes for the Sun to go from its highest point in the sky on one day to its highest point in the sky on the next day, and we divide that time into 24 hours.

A **sidereal day** is defined as the time it takes for Earth to rotate *exactly* 360° about its axis with respect to the distant stars.

5) When does Earth rotate a greater amount, during a solar day or during a sidereal day?

6) Complete the sentences below by using the words provided in the parentheses ().

Since Earth must rotate a little _____ (more/less) during a solar day, it will take _____ (more/less) time to complete a solar day than a sidereal day.

Imagine that at some time in the future the direction that Earth orbits the Sun is somehow reversed so that Earth now orbits the Sun approximately 1° *clockwise* each day. However, the rotation about its own axis remains counterclockwise at the same rate.

7) In the space below, create a sketch similar to Figure 1 to depict this imaginary situation.

8) Through how many degrees will Earth now rotate in a *sidereal* day?

9) Through how many degrees will Earth now rotate in a *solar* day?

10) Is a sidereal day now longer, shorter, or the same length as a sidereal day was before we changed Earth's orbital direction?

11) Is a solar day now longer, shorter, or the same length as a solar day was before we changed Earth's orbital direction?

12) Which will take longer, a solar or a sidereal day?

For all parts of this activity, it is helpful to imagine that the stars are so bright (or our Sun so dim) that the stars can be seen during the day so that your sky might appear as in Figure 1.

Part I: Daily Motion

On December 1, at noon, you are looking toward the south and see the Sun among the stars of the constellation Scorpius as shown in Figure 1.

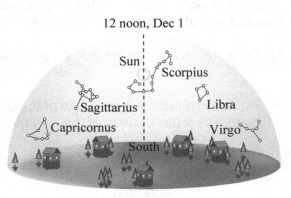

12 noon, Dec 1

Figure 1

1) At 3 P.M. that afternoon, will the Sun appear among the stars of the constellation Capricornus, Sagittarius, Scorpius, Libra, or Virgo?

2) Two students are discussing their answers to Question 1.

Student 1: *The Sun moves from the east through the southern part of the sky and then to the west. By 3 P.M. it will have moved from being high in the southern sky to the west into the constellation Libra.*

Student 2: *You're forgetting that stars and constellations, like those in Figure 1, will rise in the east, move through the southern sky, and then set in the west just like the Sun. So the Sun and Scorpius will both have moved together into the western part of the sky where Libra is now by 3 P.M.*

Do you agree or disagree with either or both of the students? Explain your reasoning.

Recall that in the celestial sphere model, the stars' daily motions result from the rotation of the celestial sphere.

3) Is it possible to model the Sun's **daily motion** by assuming that the Sun is fixed to the celestial sphere and is carried along its path across the sky by the sphere's rotation? Explain why or why not.

Part II: Monthly Changes

By careful observation of the Sun's position in the sky throughout the year, we find that the celestial sphere rotates slightly more than 360° every 24 hours. Figure 2 shows the same view of the sky (as Figure 1) but on December 2 at noon. For comparison, the view from the previous day at the same time is also shown in gray.

4) Draw the location of the Sun as accurately as possible in Figure 2.

5) Figure 3 shows the same view of the sky (as Figure 1) one month later on January 1 at noon. Draw the location of the Sun as accurately as possible in this figure.

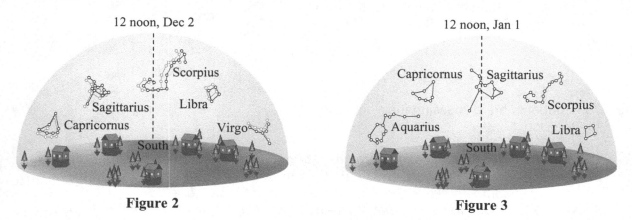

Figure 2   **Figure 3**

6) Two students are discussing their answers to Questions 4 and 5.

   Student 1:   *The Sun will always lie along the dotted line in the figures when it's noon.*
   Student 2:   *But, we saw in Question 3 that the Sun's motion can be modeled by assuming it is stuck to the celestial sphere. The Sun must, therefore, stay in Scorpius.*
   Student 1:   *If that were true, then by March the Sun would be setting at noon. The Sun must shift a little along the celestial sphere each day so that in 30 days it has moved toward the east into the next constellation.*

   Do you agree or disagree with either or both of the students? Explain your reasoning.

Part III: The Ecliptic

The zodiacal constellations were of special interest to ancient astronomers because these are the constellations through which the Sun moves throughout the year. These ancient astronomers imagined that the Sun was fixed to the celestial sphere to account for daily motions, but they also imagined that the Sun could move slightly along the sphere from day to day. The Sun's position on the celestial sphere (among the stars in the constellation Scorpius) on December 1 is shown in Figure 4.

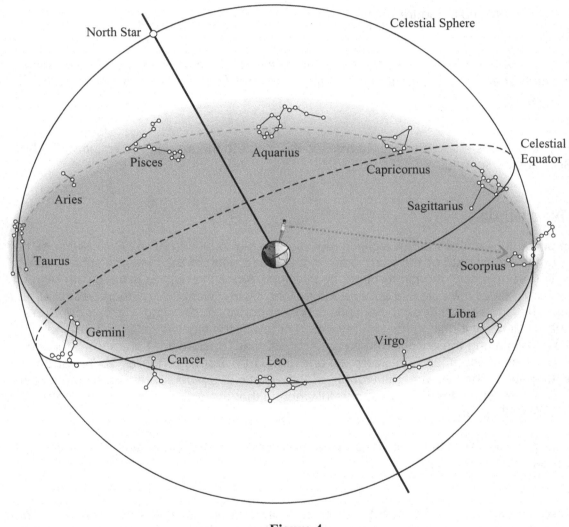

Figure 4

7) On Figure 4, draw where the Sun will be located on the celestial sphere on January 1. Label this position "Jan 1."

8) On Figure 4, for the other constellations, draw in the Sun and label the constellation with the approximate date that the Sun will be located there.

The line drawn through these constellations, tracing out the Sun's annual path, is called the **ecliptic.**

9) Label the ecliptic in Figure 4.

10) About how many times does the celestial sphere rotate in the time it takes the Sun to move between two adjacent constellations (i.e., 1/12 of the way around) along the ecliptic?

11) How long does it take the Sun to make one complete trip around the ecliptic (i.e., from Scorpius to Scorpius)?

Part IV: Wrap-Up

It is important to realize that the ecliptic represents an *annual* drift of the Sun and does not represent the daily path of the Sun. Instead, it is the rotation of the celestial sphere that model's the Sun's daily motion through the sky. Also, since the ecliptic is tilted with respect to the rotation axis of the celestial sphere, the ecliptic slowly "wobbles" as the celestial sphere rotates. The Sun's position on the ecliptic is only important in deciding whether the Sun's daily path will carry it high in the sky (summer) or low in the sky (winter). In Figure 5a, the Sun's position along the ecliptic and its path for one day (dashed line) are shown for two different dates: December 1 (in Scorpius) and June 1 (in Taurus). Figures 5b, 5c, and 5d show the path of the Sun and the wobble of the ecliptic at six-hour intervals as the celestial sphere rotates. Study these figures, carefully noting that the ecliptic and Sun are both carried by the celestial sphere.

12) On Figure 5d, label the ecliptic (Sun's annual path) and the Sun's daily path for December 1 and June 1.

13) Which Figure (5a, 5b, 5c, or 5d) shows the Sun at noon, low in the southern sky, when it would be among the stars of the constellation Scorpius?

14) Which Figure (5a, 5b, 5c, or 5d) shows the Sun at noon, high in the southern sky, when it would be among the stars of the constellation Taurus?

December 1 (Sun in Scorpius)
and
June 1 (Sun in Taurus)

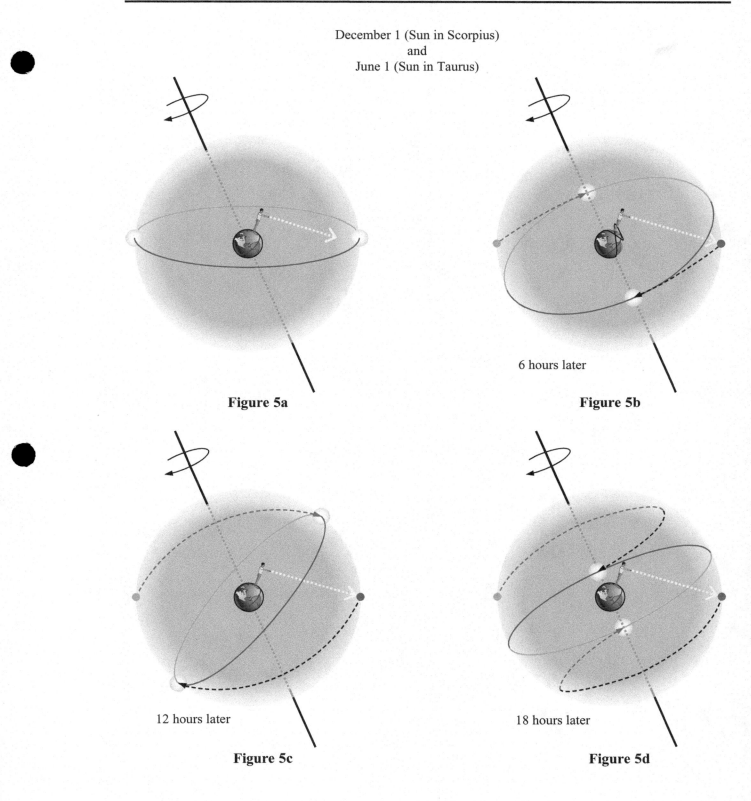

Figure 5a

6 hours later

Figure 5b

12 hours later

Figure 5c

18 hours later

Figure 5d

Consider the overhead-view star map for July at midnight shown in Figure 1. In particular, notice that the directions of north and east have been identified and that the names of different star groups (constellations) have been provided.

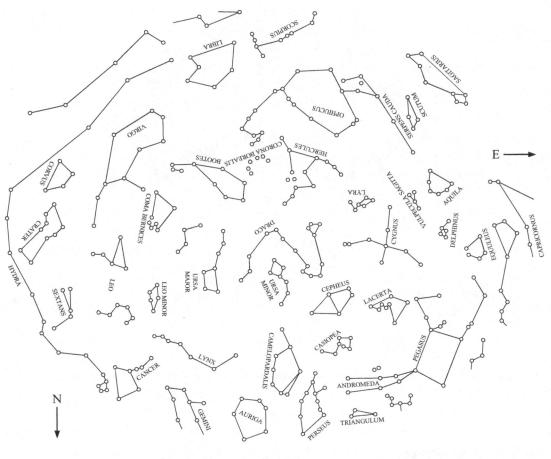

Figure 1

1) Which star group will appear highest in the night sky at this particular time?

2) Figure 2 shows a south-facing horizon view star map for July at midnight. What is the name of the star group that appears highest in the sky on this south-facing horizon view star map? (Hint: refer to the names provided in Figure 1.)

Figure 2

3) How would you have to hold, rotate, fold, and/or change the overhead-view star map shown in Figure 1 so that it could be used as a south-facing star map like the one provided in Figure 2?

4) How would your answer to the previous question change if you wanted to use the star map from Figure 1 as a north-facing map?

5) Do you still agree with your answer to Question 1? Why or why not?

6) When looking at the overhead-view star map from Figure 1,

   a) on what part of the map (left, right, top, bottom, or center) is the star group that will appear highest in the night sky? What is the name of this star group?

   b) on what part of the map (left, right, top, bottom, or center) is the star group that will appear near the southern horizon? What is the name of this star group?

   c) on what part of the map (left, right, top, bottom, or center) is the star group that will appear near the eastern horizon? What is the name of this star group?

Part I: Equal Area in Equal Time Intervals

Kepler's second law of planetary motion states that a line joining a planet and the Sun sweeps out equal amounts of area in equal intervals of time.

Imagine the situation shown at the right in which a planet is moving in a perfectly circular orbit around its companion star. Note that the time between each position shown is exactly one month.

1) Does this planet obey Kepler's second law? How do you know?

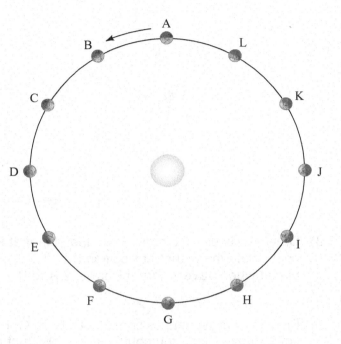

2) If you were carefully watching this planet during the entire orbit, would the speed of the planet be increasing, decreasing, or staying the same? How do you know?

In the drawing below, a planet that obeys Kepler's second law is shown at nine different locations (A–I) during the planet's orbit around its companion star.

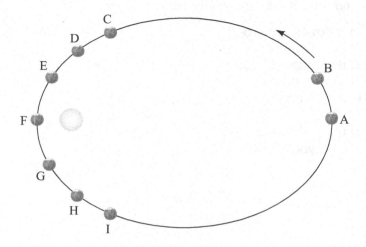

3) Draw two lines: one connecting the planet at Position A to the star and a second line connecting the planet at Position B to the star. Shade in the area swept out by the planet when traveling from Positions A to B.

4) Pick any two planet positions (C, D, E, F, G, H, I)—note, they do not have to be consecutive—that you could use to construct a swept-out area that would have approximately the same area as the one you shaded in for Question 3. Shade in the second swept-out area using the planet positions that you chose. Note: Your shaded area needs to be only roughly the same size; no calculations or quantitative estimates are required.

5) How would the time it takes the planet to travel from Position A to Position B compare (greater than, less than, or equal to) to the time it takes to travel between the two positions you selected in Question 4? Explain your reasoning.

6) During which of the two time intervals for which you sketched the shaded areas in Questions 3 and 4 is the distance traveled by the planet greater?

7) During which of the two time intervals for which you sketched the shaded areas in Questions 3 and 4 would the planet be traveling faster? Explain your reasoning.

Part II: Kepler's Second Law and the Speed of the Planets

The drawing below shows another planet's orbit. In this case, the twelve positions shown (A–L) are each exactly one month apart. As before, the planet shown obeys Kepler's second law.

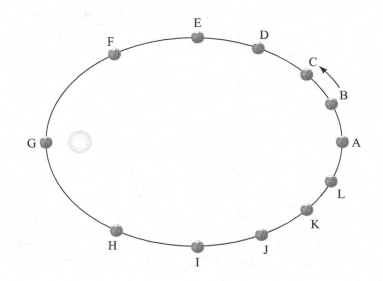

8) Does the planet appear to be traveling the same distance each month?

9) At which position would the planet have been traveling the fastest? The slowest? Explain your reasoning.

10) At Position D, is the speed of the planet increasing or decreasing as time goes on? Explain your reasoning.

11) Provide a concise statement that describes the relationship that exists between a planet's orbital speed and the planet's distance from its companion star.

Part III: Kepler's Second Law and Eccentricity

Consider the table below listing the orbit eccentricities for objects in the solar system. Recall that an orbit with an eccentricity of zero is perfectly circular whereas the highly elliptical orbits shown in Parts I and II would have a high eccentricity of approximately 0.90.

Object	Eccentricity of Orbit
Mercury	0.206
Venus	0.007
Earth	0.016
Mars	0.093
Jupiter	0.048
Saturn	0.054
Uranus	0.047
Neptune	0.008
Pluto	0.248

12) Which of the three orbits shown below (A, B, or C) would you say most closely matches the shape of Earth's orbit around the Sun? Explain your reasoning.

13) Which of the objects listed in the table above would experience the largest change in orbital speed and which would experience the smallest change in orbital speed?

14) Describe the extent to which you think Earth's orbital speed changes throughout a year? Explain your reasoning.

Kepler's third law describes the relationship between how long it takes a planet to orbit a star (orbital period) and how far away that planet is from the star (orbital distance). In this activity, we investigate an imaginary planetary system that has an average star, like the Sun, located at the center of the orbits of two planets. A huge Jupiter-like planet named Esus orbits close to the star, while a small Earth-like, terrestrial planet named Sulis is in an orbit far away around the star. Use this information when answering the next four questions. If you're not sure of the correct answers to Questions 1–4, just take a guess. We'll return to these questions later in this activity.

1) Which of the two planets (Esus or Sulis) do you think will move around the central star in the least amount of time? Explain your reasoning.

Esus, b/c it orbits close to the star.

2) If Esus and Sulis were to switch positions, would your answer to Question 1 change? If so, how? If not, why not?

Yes, b/c their orbits would change

3) Do you think the orbital period for Esus would increase, decrease, or stay the same if its mass were increased? Explain your reasoning.

Stay the same because the speed of orbit depends on the mass of the central star

4) Imagine both Esus and Sulis were in orbit around the same central star at the same distance and that their orbital positions would never intersect (so that they would never collide). Which of the two planets (Esus or Sulis) do you think will move around the central star in the least amount of time? Explain your reasoning.

Same amount of time, same central star and orbit is the same

The graph below illustrates how the orbital period (expressed in years) and orbital distance (expressed in astronomical units, AU) of a planet are related.

5) According to the graph, would you say that the orbital period of planets appears to increase, decrease, or stay the same as their orbital distance is increased?

   increase

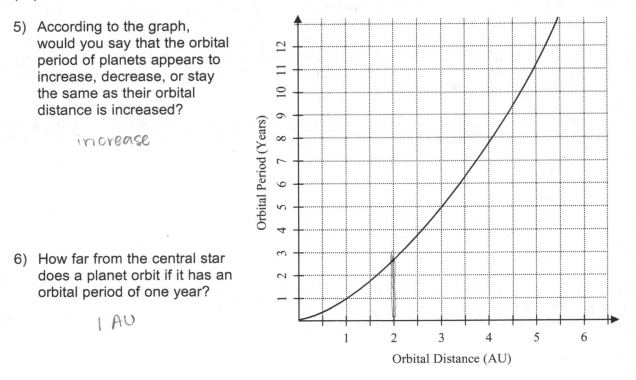

Orbital Period (Years)

Orbital Distance (AU)

6) How far from the central star does a planet orbit if it has an orbital period of one year?

   I AU

7) How long does it take a planet to complete one orbit if it is twice the distance from the central star as the planet described in Question 6?

   ~ 2.8 orbital periods

8) Based on your results from Questions 6 and 7, which of the following best describes how a planet's orbital period will change (if at all) when its distance to the central star is doubled? Circle your choice.

   a) The planet's orbital period will decrease by half.

   b) The planet's orbital period will not change.

   c) The planet's orbital period will double.

   d) The planet's orbital period will more than double.

In the table below we have provided the orbital distances, orbital periods, and masses for the eight planets in our solar system.

Planet	Orbital Distance (in astronomical units—AU)	Orbital Period (in years)	Planet Mass (in units of Earth's mass)
Mercury	0.38	0.24	0.06
Venus	0.72	0.61	0.82
Earth	1.0	1.0	1.0
Mars	1.52	1.88	0.11
Jupiter	5.20	11.86	318
Saturn	9.54	29.46	95.2
Uranus	19.2	84.01	14.54
Neptune	30.06	164.8	17.15

9) What is the name of the planet that you identified the orbital distance for in Question 6?

earth?

10) Using the information provided in the table above and on the graph on the previous page, which of the answers below best describes how a planet's mass will affect its orbital period. Circle your choice.

a) Planets that have small masses have longer orbital periods than planets with large masses.

b) Planets with the same mass will also have the same orbital period.

c) Planets that have large masses have longer orbital periods than planets with small masses.

d) A planet's mass does not affect the orbital period of a planet.

Explain your reasoning and cite a specific example from the table or graph to support your choice.

the diff in mass between jupiter + saturn is 318 to 95.2 but the larger the mass here the faster the orbital period but Mar's is mass is .11 but its orbital period is 1.88 which would say smaller masses are a faster orbital period

11) A student in your class makes the following comment about the relationship between the location of planets in our solar system and their orbital period and mass.

Student: *As we look at planets farther away from the Sun than Mercury, we see that their distances get bigger and that the mass of the planets is also getting larger. So I think that the farther away a planet is from the Sun, the more massive it will be and the longer it will take to go around the Sun.*

Do you agree or disagree with this student? Which planet(s) listed in the table above support your answer? Explain your reasoning.

NO

12) Review your answers to Questions 1–4. Do you still agree with the answers you provided? If not, describe (next to your original answers) how you would change the answers you gave initially.

Part I: The Force of Gravity

Newton's law of universal gravitation describes the attractive gravitational force that exists between any two bodies with the following equation:

$$F_G = \frac{GMm}{r^2}$$

G is the gravitational constant (which for this activity you can assign a value of 1). **M** and **m** are the masses of the two objects attracting one another, and **r** is the distance from the center of one object to the center of the other object.

1) Given that Earth is much larger and more massive than the Moon, how does the strength of the gravitational force that the Moon exerts on Earth compare to the gravitational force that Earth exerts on the Moon? Explain your reasoning.

   The gravitational force would be the same of each on the other because Fg takes the same info into account.

2) Consider the following debate between two students about their answer to the previous question.

   Student 1: *To calculate the strength of each gravitational force, you have to use both masses and the distance between Earth and the Moon in the equation. Because each calculation uses the same numbers, you will get the same gravitational force on Earth and on the Moon, so they are equal.*

   Student 2: *I disagree. I said that Earth exerts the stronger force because it is way bigger than the Moon. Because its mass is bigger, the gravitational force Earth exerts has to be bigger too. I think you are confusing Newton's third law with the law of gravity.*

   Do you agree or disagree with either or both of the students? Explain your reasoning.

   I agree w/ student 1 b/c the equation for gravitational force has the same info for both.

3) How would the strength of the force between the Moon and Earth change if the mass of the Moon were somehow made two times greater than its current mass?

Double

Part II: Force–Distance Relationship

In the picture below, a spaceprobe traveling from Earth to Mars is shown at the halfway point between the two (not to scale).

X₆ ● Mars

X

🛰 Spaceprobe

 X∞4
Earth

4) On the diagram, clearly label the location where the spaceprobe would be when the gravitational force <u>by Earth</u> on the spaceprobe is strongest? Explain your reasoning.

Because the smaller the distance the greater F_G

↓

5) On the diagram, clearly label the location where the spaceprobe would be when the gravitational force <u>by Mars</u> on the spaceprobe is strongest. Explain your reasoning.

6) When the spacecraft is at the halfway point, how does the strength of the gravitational force on the spaceprobe by Earth compare with the strength of the gravitational force on the spaceprobe by Mars? Explain your reasoning.

The F_G of Earth + spaceprobe is greater b/c the Earth has a greater mass

Mars 11% of earth's mass

7) Two students are discussing their answer to the previous question.

Student 1: *Since the spaceprobe is exactly halfway between Earth and Mars, the strength of the gravitational forces would be the same since the distances are the same.* ✕

Student 2: *You're right that the distances are the same, but you're forgetting about mass. The Earth is much more massive than the Moon* (mars) *so, the strength of the gravitational force on the spaceprobe by Earth has to be bigger than the strength of the gravitational force on the spaceprobe by Mars.*

Do you agree or disagree with either or both of the students? Explain your reasoning.

agree w/ 2   b/c F_G takes into account mass

8) If the spaceprobe had lost all ability to control its motion and was sitting at rest at the midpoint between Earth and Mars, would the spacecraft stay at the midpoint or would it start to move?

Move

If you think it stays at the midpoint, explain why it would not move.

If you think it would move, then: (a) Describe the direction it would move; (b) describe if it would speed up or slow down; (c) describe how the net (or total) force on the spaceprobe would change during this motion; and (d) identify when/where the spaceprobe would experience the greatest acceleration.

a) toward the earth
b) speed up
c) net force get greater
d) right next to the earth

9) Imagine that you need to completely stop the motion of the spaceprobe and have it remain at rest while you perform a shutdown and restart procedure. You have decided that the best place to carry out this procedure would be at the position where the net (or total) gravitational force on the spaceprobe by Mars and Earth would be zero. On the diagram, label the location where you would perform this procedure. (Make your best guess; there is no need to perform any calculations here.) Explain the reasoning behind your choice.

b/c you move closer to mars the F_G felt by mars gets larger + F_G felt by earth gets smaller but holds more because its mass is much bigger.

1) Which value, apparent magnitude, or absolute magnitude:

   a) tells us how bright an object will appear from Earth?

   apparent magnitude

   b) tells us about the object's actual brightness?

   luminosity / absolute magnitude

2) The full Moon has an apparent magnitude of −12.6, and when Mars is at its brightest in the night sky, its apparent magnitude is +2.0.

   a) Which of the two objects has the bigger apparent magnitude number?

   Mars

   b) Which object will look brighter from Earth, the full Moon or Mars? How do you know?

   magnitude

   c) Imagine a new object has been discovered that, from Earth, appears dimmer than Mars. Make up a possible apparent magnitude number for this object.

   ✱ 3.0

3) Consider the following debate between two students.

   agree

   Student 1: *I think a star with an apparent magnitude number of −2.0 would look brighter than a star with an apparent magnitude number of +1.0.*
   Student 2: *I disagree. You don't understand the number scale for apparent and absolute magnitude. The bigger the number the brighter the star. So the +1.0 star would look brighter than the −2.0 star.*

   Do you agree or disagree with either or both of the students? Explain your reasoning.

4) Star Y appears much brighter than Star Z when viewed from Earth, but is found to actually give off much less light. Assign a set of possible values for the apparent and absolute magnitudes of these stars that would be consistent with the information given in the previous statement. Explain your reasoning.

Star Y   m: 7   Star Z   m: 9

        M: 5   M: 2

5) The star Alissa has an apparent magnitude of 0.1 and is located about 250 parsecs away from Earth. Which of the following is most likely the absolute magnitude for Alissa:

a) **−6.9** *(circled)*

b) 0.1   m = .1

c) 7.1

Explain your reasoning.

absolute is closer so it will be brighter than apparent lets on and will be more neg # for absolute magnitude

6) Refer to the following table for Questions 6a–6d:

	Apparent Magnitude	Absolute Magnitude
Star A:	1	1
Star B:	1	2
Star C:	5	4
Star D:	4	4

(margin notes: C — exactly, less, more, exactly)

a) Which object appears brighter from Earth: Star C or Star D? Explain your reasoning.

D

b) Which object is actually brighter: Star A or Star D? Explain your reasoning.

A

c) For Stars A–D, state whether the star is closer than, farther than, or exactly 10 parsecs away from Earth. Explain your reasoning.

d) Would the apparent magnitude number of Star A increase, decrease, or stay the same, if it were located at a distance of 40 parsecs? What about the absolute magnitude number? Explain your reasoning.

always measured at 10 pcs

dimmer —> increase

Stay the same

7) Star F is known to have an apparent magnitude of −26.7 and an absolute magnitude of 4.8. Where might this star be located? What is the name of this star? Explain your reasoning.

dim

bright

closest to the earth, the sun

Part I: Stars in the Sky

Consider the diagram to the right.

1) Imagine that you are looking at the stars from Earth in January. Use a straightedge or a ruler to draw a straight line from Earth in January, through the Nearby Star (Star A), out to the Distant Stars. Which of the distant stars would appear closest to Star A in your night sky in January? Circle this distant star and label it "Jan."

2) Repeat Question 1 for July and label the distant star "July."

3) In the box below, the same distant stars are shown as you would see them in the night sky. Draw a small × to indicate the position of Star A as seen in January and label it "Star A Jan."

4) In the same box, draw another × to indicate the position of Star A as seen in July and label it "Star A July."

In astronomy, **parallax** is the apparent motion of a nearby object, relative to distance objects, due to the motion of Earth around the Sun.

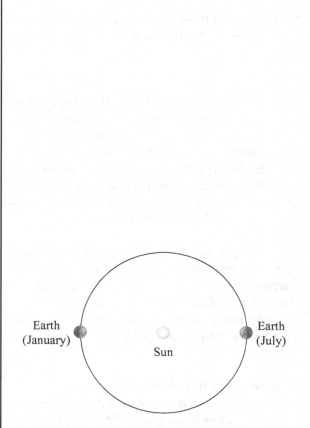

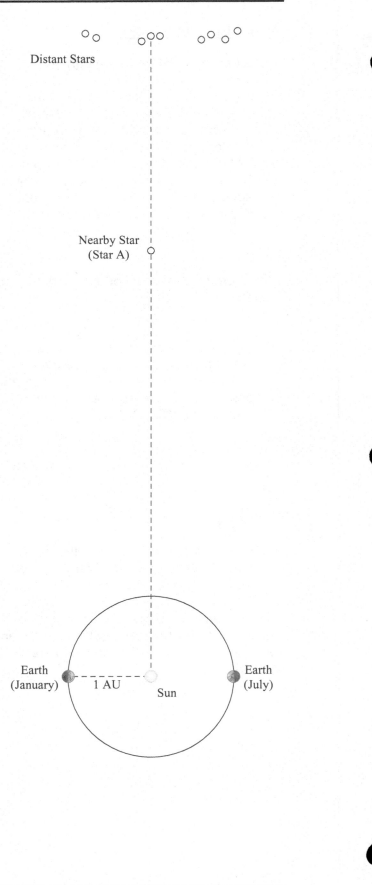

Distant Stars

Nearby Star
(Star A)

Earth
(January)

1 AU

Sun

Earth
(July)

5) Imagine you were observing two stars (C and D) that both exhibit parallax. As Earth orbits the Sun during the year, you observe that Star C appears to move by a greater amount than Star D. Does this mean that Star C is closer or farther from you than Star D? If you're not sure, just take a guess. We'll return to this question later in this activity.

Part II: What's a Parsec?

Consider the diagram to the right.

6) Starting from Earth in January, draw a line through Star A to the top of the page.

7) There is now a narrow triangle, created by the line you drew, the dotted line from the Sun, through Star A to the distant stars, and the dotted line from the Sun to Earth. The small angle, just below Star A, formed by the two longest sides of this triangle is called the **parallax angle** for Star A. Label this angle "p_A."

Knowing a star's parallax angle allows us to calculate the distance to the star. Since even the nearest stars are still very far away, parallax angles are extremely small. These parallax angles are measured in "arcseconds" where an arcsecond is 1/3600 of 1 degree.

To describe the distances to stars, astronomers use a unit of length called the **parsec.** One parsec is defined as the distance to a star that has a **par**allax angle of exactly 1 arc**sec**ond.

Note: 1 parsec is 206,265 AU. Since the distance from the Sun to even the closest star is so much greater than 1 AU, we can consider the distance from Earth to a star and the distance from the Sun to that star to be approximately equal.

8) If the parallax angle for Star A (p_A) is 1 arcsecond, what is the distance from the Sun to Star A? (Hint: Use parsec as your unit of distance.) Label this distance on the diagram.

9) Is a parsec a unit of length or a unit of angle? It can't be both.

Part III: Distances

10) On your diagram from Part II, draw a second star along the dotted line farther from the Sun than Star A and label this faraway star "Star B." Repeat steps 6 and 7 from Part II, except label the parallax angle for this Star B with p_B.

11) Which star, the closer one (Star A) or the farther one (Star B), has the larger parallax angle?

12) Consider the following debate between two students regarding the relationship between parallax angle and the distance we measure to a star.

Student 1: *If the distance to the star is more than 1 parsec, then the parallax angle must be more than 1 arcsecond. So a star that is many parsecs away will have a large parallax angle.*

Student 2: *If we drew a diagram for a star that was much more than 1 parsec away from us, the triangle in the diagram would be pointier than the one we just drew in Part II. That should make the parallax angle smaller for a star farther away.*

Do you agree or disagree with either or both of the students? Explain your reasoning.

13) Check your answers to Question 5 and resolve any discrepancies.

We are often unable to **directly** measure distances to faraway objects in our night sky. However, we can obtain the distances to relatively nearby stars by using their parallax angles. Because even these stars are very far away (up to about 500 parsecs), the parallax angles for these stars are very small. They are measured in units of **arcseconds**, where 1 arcsecond is 1/3600 of 1 degree. To give you a sense of how small this angle is, the thin edge of a credit card, when viewed from one football field away, covers an angle of about 1 arcsecond.

Consider the starfield drawing shown in Figure 1. This represents a tiny patch of our night sky. In this drawing we will imagine that the angle separating Stars A and B is just 1/2 of an arcsecond.

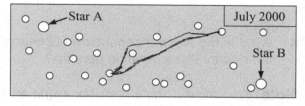

Figure 1

In Figure 2 (see the final page of the activity), there are drawings of this starfield taken at different times during the year. One star in the field moves back and forth across the star field (exhibits parallax) with respect to the other, more distant stars.

1) Using Figure 2, determine which star exhibits parallax. Circle that star on each picture in Figure 2.

2) In Figure 1, draw a line that shows the range of motion for the star you saw exhibiting parallax in the drawings from Figure 2. Label the end points of this line with the months when the star appears at those end points.

3) How many times bigger is the separation between Stars A and B compared to the distance between the end points of the line showing the range of the motion for the star exhibiting parallax?

A−B is a larger seperation

4) What is the angular separation between the end points that you marked in Figure 1 for the nearby star exhibiting parallax? *about ¼ of an arcsecond*

Note: We define a star's **parallax angle as half** the angular separation between the end points of the star's angular motion.

5) What is the parallax angle for the nearby star exhibiting parallax from Question 1?

⅛ arcsecond

Note: We define 1 **parsec** as the distance to an object that has a **par**allax angle of 1 arc**sec**ond. For a star with a parallax angle of 2 arcseconds, the distance to the star from Earth would be 1/2 of a parsec.

6) For a star with a parallax angle of 1/2 of an arcsecond, what is its distance from us (in parsecs)?

2 parsecs

7) For a star with a parallax angle of 1/4 of an arcsecond, what is its distance from us (in parsecs)?

4 parsecs

8) What is the distance from us to the nearby star exhibiting parallax in the drawings from Figure 2? (Hint: Consider your answer to Question 5.)

   a) 1 parsec

   b) 2 parsecs

   c) 4 parsecs

   d) 8 parsecs

   e) 16 parsecs

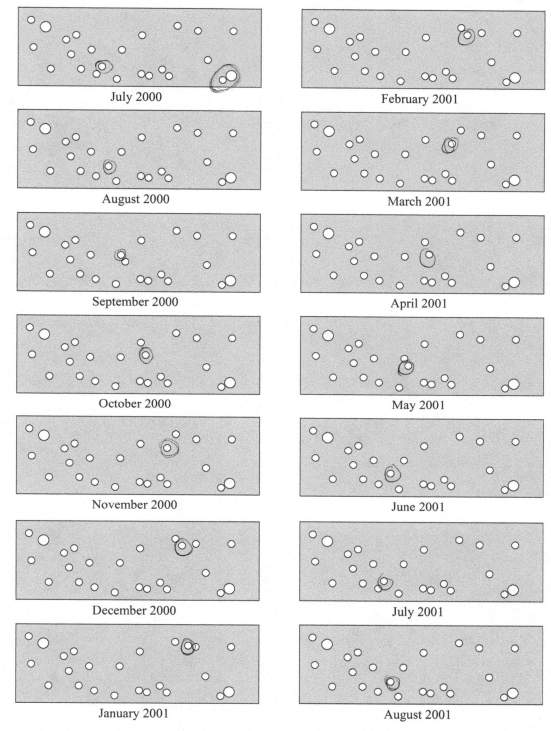

July 2000

August 2000

September 2000

October 2000

November 2000

December 2000

January 2001

February 2001

March 2001

April 2001

May 2001

June 2001

July 2001

August 2001

Figure 2

Part I: Magnitudes and Star Distances

Below is a table of four stars along with their apparent and absolute magnitudes. Use this table to answer the following questions.

	Apparent Magnitude	Absolute Magnitude	Distance
Star A:	0	0	10
Star B:	0	2	< 10
Star C:	5	4	> 10
Star D:	4	4	10

1) Which object appears brighter from Earth: Star C, Star D, or neither? Explain your reasoning.

    D, apparent magnitude is lower

2) Which object is more luminous: Star C, Star D, or ⟨neither?⟩ Explain your reasoning.

    same ↓ absolute magnitude

3) Star B has an apparent magnitude of 0, which tells us how bright it appears from Earth. Star B has an absolute magnitude of 2, which tells us how bright it would appear if it were at a distance of 10 parsecs (about 33 light-years).

    Where would Star B appear brighter, at its actual distance or if it were at a distance of 10 parsecs? Explain your reasoning.

    ↓ lower magnitude

4) Is Star B ⟨closer⟩ than 10 parsecs, farther than 10 parsecs, or exactly 10 parsecs away? Record your answer in the table above, and explain your reasoning.

    brighter apparent mag

5) Fill in the distance column of the above table with closer than 10 parsecs, farther than 10 parsecs, or exactly 10 parsecs away. Explain your reasoning for the distances you recorded for Stars A, C, and D.

Part II: Spectroscopic Parallax

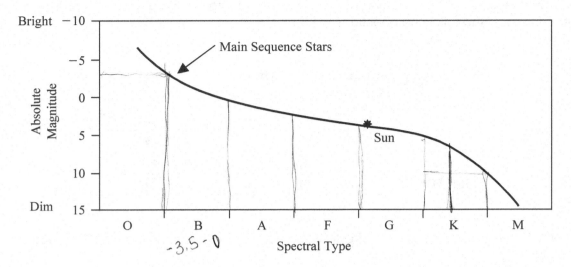

Below is a table giving both the apparent magnitude and spectral type for five **main sequence** stars. For each star, do the following:

6) Using the above H–R diagram, estimate the absolute magnitude for each star and write your answer in the absolute magnitude column of the table below.

7) Complete the distance column in the table below by classifying each star as being *closer than, farther than, or exactly 10 parsecs away*. This procedure, called spectroscopic parallax, provides astronomers with another way to measure the distance to stars.

Star	Apparent Magnitude	Spectral Type	Absolute Magnitude	Distance Estimate
Star 1	15.0	K	7.5	>10
Star 2	0.1	G	4.5	<10
Star 3	−1.0	A	1	< 10
Star 4	5.0	B	−1.75	>10
Star 5	−8.0	B	−1.75	<10

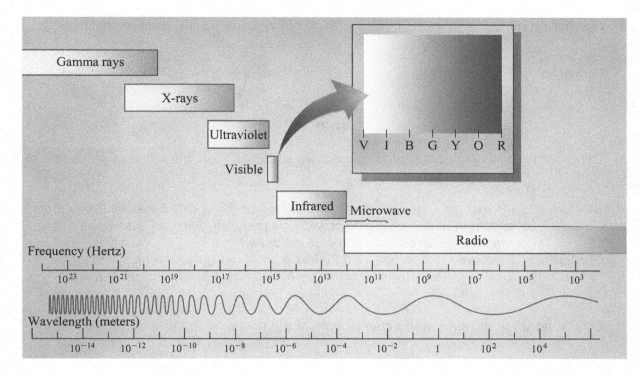

1) The electromagnetic spectrum of light is often arranged in terms of frequency. Which one of the following has the highest frequency (*circle one*)?

visible   microwaves   infrared   gamma
 light   light   rays
          radio   X-rays   ultraviolet
          waves   light

2) The electromagnetic spectrum of light can also be arranged in terms of wavelengths. Which one of the following has the longest wavelength (*circle one*)?

visible   X-rays   ultraviolet   unfrared
 light   light   light
          gamma   microwaves   radio
          rays   waves

3) Which of the following types of light travels at the fastest speed (*circle your answer(s)*)? Explain your answer.

ultraviolet   X-rays   gamma   visible
 light   rays   light
          microwaves   radio   infrared
                              waves   light

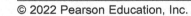

4) Another property of light is the energy. Which of the following has the greatest energy (*circle one*)?

ultraviolet   X-rays   gamma   visible
  light   rays   light
            microwaves   radio   infrared
                                   waves   light

5) Consider the following discussion between two students about the different properties of light.

Student 1: *I think I get how light works. If you look at the chart of the electromagnetic spectrum, it shows that light with a higher frequency will also have a long wavelength. But it all has the same speed.*

Student 2: *I disagree. If one type of light has a lot of energy and a high frequency, it will have a faster speed than light that has a lower energy and a low frequency.*

Do you agree or disagree with either or both of the students? Explain your reasoning.

6) Complete the following sentence describing the relationship among the energy, frequency, and wavelength of light, using the words *highest, lowest, longest,* and/or *shortest.*

*The portion of the electromagnetic spectrum of light with the **greatest** energy has the _____ frequency and the _____ wavelengths.*

7) For each statement (a–d) provided below, circle the word choice that correctly describes how the two forms of light compare.

a) Infrared light has <u>greater / lesser</u> energy than ultraviolet light.

b) X-ray photons have <u>longer / shorter</u> wavelengths than gamma ray photons.

c) Visible electromagnetic radiation has a <u>higher / lower</u> frequency than radio electromagnetic radiation.

d) Infrared light has a <u>faster / slower / same</u> speed than microwave light.

8) Of all the types of light the Sun gives off, it emits the greatest amount of light at visible light wavelengths. If the Sun were to cool off dramatically and as a result start giving off mainly light at wavelengths longer than visible light, how would the frequency, energy, and speed of this light given off by the Sun also be different? Explain your reasoning.

The drawing below illustrates the amount that different wavelengths of light are able to penetrate down through Earth's atmosphere. The shaded regions are used in this drawing to depict different layers in Earth's atmosphere. Notice that the atmosphere can be completely transparent to light at some wavelengths (all three lines passing through the atmosphere to the surface of Earth) and yet can also completely absorb other wavelengths of light (all three lines stopping in the atmosphere before reaching Earth's surface).

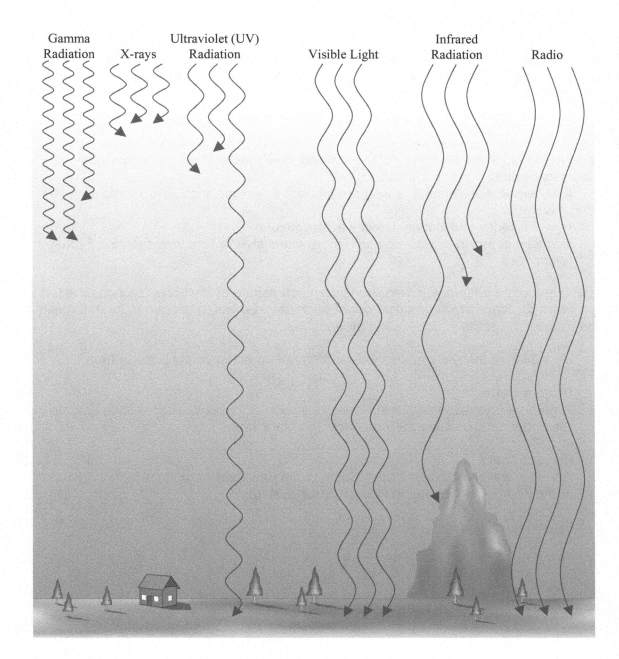

1) Which, if any, of the different wavelengths of light (electromagnetic radiation) shown in the image on the previous page are able to *completely* penetrate Earth's atmosphere and reach the surface?

2) Which, if any, of the different wavelengths of light (electromagnetic radiation) shown in the image on the previous page only *partially* penetrate Earth's atmosphere and reach the surface?

3) Which, if any, of the different wavelengths of light (electromagnetic radiation) shown in the image on the previous page are *completely* absorbed in Earth's atmosphere and never reach the surface?

4) Federal funding agencies form committees to decide which telescope projects will receive funds for construction. When deciding which projects will be funded, the committees must consider:
   - that certain wavelengths of light are blocked from reaching Earth's surface by the atmosphere,
   - how efficiently telescopes detect wavelengths, and
   - that telescopes in space are much more expensive to construct than Earth-based telescopes.

Use these three criteria when you consider each pairing of telescope proposals listed below (a–d). State which proposal out of *each pair* you would choose to fund. Explain the reasoning behind your decision *for each pair.*

   a) Which of the two proposals described below would you choose to fund?

Project Delta:
A gamma ray wavelength telescope, located in Antarctica, which will be used to look for evidence to indicate the presence of a black hole.

Project Theta:
A visible wavelength telescope, located on a university campus, which will be used in the search for planets outside the solar system.

Explain your reasoning.

b) Which of the two proposals described below would you choose to fund?

Project Beta:
An X-ray wavelength telescope, located near the North Pole, which will be used to examine the Sun.

Project Alpha:
An infrared wavelength telescope, placed on a satellite in orbit around Earth, which will be used to view supernovae.

Explain your reasoning.

c) Which of the two proposals described below would you choose to fund?

Project Rho:
A UV wavelength telescope, placed on a satellite in orbit around Earth, which will be used to look at distant galaxies.

Project Sigma:
A visible wavelength telescope, placed on a satellite in orbit around Earth, which will be used to observe a pair of binary stars located in the constellation Ursa Major.

Explain your reasoning.

d) Which of the two proposals described below would you choose to fund?

Project Zeta:
A radio wavelength telescope, located in the high elevation mountains of Chile, which will be used to detect potential communications from distant civilizations outside our solar system.

Project Epsilon:
An infrared wavelength telescope, placed on the floor of the Mojave Desert, which will be used to view newly forming stars (protostars) in the Orion nebula.

Explain your reasoning.

LECTURE-TUTORIALS FOR INTRODUCTORY ASTRONOMY
FOURTH EDITION

An interferometer is a group of telescopes that work together as a single telescope. Because an interferometer consists of multiple telescopes, it can make observations that are not possible with a single telescope.

The **light-collecting power** (LCP) of an interferometer is a number that indicates how much light it can collect. The greater the LCP, the better the interferometer it is able to detect objects that appear dim. The equation for the LCP of an interferometer is $LCP = N \times A$. In this equation, N is the number of individual telescopes in the interferometer, and A is the average area of the telescopes.

The Light-Collecting Power (LCP) and Number of Telescopes (N) of three interferometers (A, B, and C) are plotted in the graph at right.

1) Rank the Light-Collecting Power (LCP) of the interferometers (A, B, and C) from greatest to least.

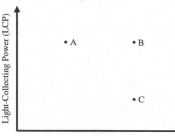

2) Which of the interferometers has the smallest telescopes? Explain your reasoning.

The **resolution** of an interferometer is a number that indicates how small are the details that the interferometer can detect. A small resolution number indicates that the interferometer can identify small details, or distinguish objects that are separated by a small distance. The equation for the resolution of an interferometer is $R = \lambda / B$. In this equation, R is the resolution, λ is the wavelength of light being observed, and B is the baseline (which is the distance between the telescopes that are farthest apart in the interferometer).

The Observed Wavelength (λ) and Baseline (B) of three interferometers (D, E, and F) are plotted in the graph at right.

3) Rank the resolution (R) of the three interferometers (D, E, and F) from smallest to largest number.

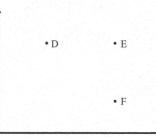

4) If all three interferometers (D, E, and F) observe the same object, which interferometer could produce images with the smallest details? Explain your reasoning.

LECTURE-TUTORIALS FOR INTRODUCTORY ASTRONOMY
                                                    FOURTH EDITION

5) Two students are discussing their answers to Questions 3 and 4:

Student 1: *I think you get a better image when the resolution is small, because then you can see small details and objects that are separated by a small amount. The resolution is the wavelength divided by the baseline, so when the wavelength is small, and the baseline is large, you get a really small resolution because that's a small number divided by a large number. That means, Interferometer F would produce images with the smallest details.*

Student 2: *I disagree. I think a large resolution is good because that means you can see a large number of details. What you said about dividing two numbers makes sense, though. So to get a large resolution, you should observe at long wavelengths with a short baseline. That means, Interferometer D would produce images with the largest number of details.*

Do you agree or disagree with either or both of the students? Explain your reasoning.

6) Consider two different interferometers whose properties are given in the table below.

	Interferometer 1	Interferometer 2
Number of Telescopes	15	5
Wavelength Observed	Long	Short
Baseline	Small	Large
Size of Telescopes	Large	Small

Compare the two interferometers by completing the blanks in the sentences below by circling the correct words or phrases.

Interferometer 1 contains a _____ (larger/smaller) number of telescopes that are _____ (larger/smaller) in size; therefore, it has a _____ (larger/smaller) LCP than Interferometer 2. Interferometer 2 has a _____ (larger/smaller) baseline and observes light at _____ (longer/shorter) wavelengths; therefore, it has a _____ (larger/smaller) resolution than Interferometer 1. So, Interferometer _____ (1/2) would be better at detecting dim objects, and Interferometer _____ (1/2) would be better at producing images with small details.

Figure 1, below, shows four different images of the same object. Each image was produced by a different interferometer. When an area of the image appears brighter, it means that more light was collected from that part of the sky.

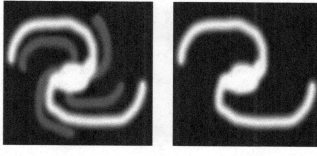

| Image A | Image B |

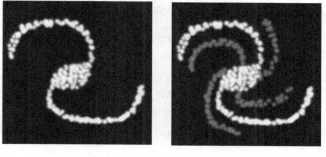

| Image C | Image D |

Figure 1

7) Match each of the interferometer descriptions below with the correct image from Figure 1.

    a. Small resolution and large LCP

    b. Small resolution and small LCP

    c. Large resolution and large LCP

    d. Large resolution and small LCP

Figure 2, below, depicts four different interferometers. The label for each interferometer includes the wavelength at which it observes the sky. The area of each large telescope is four times the area of each small telescope and the baseline of Interferometers H and J is two times the baseline of Interferometers G and I.

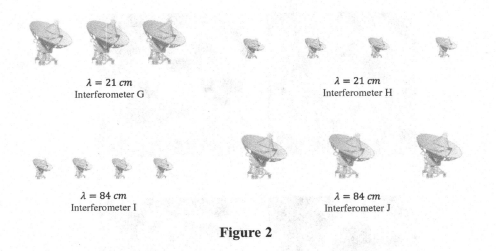

$\lambda = 21\ cm$
Interferometer G

$\lambda = 21\ cm$
Interferometer H

$\lambda = 84\ cm$
Interferometer I

$\lambda = 84\ cm$
Interferometer J

Figure 2

8) Rank the LCP of the interferometers shown in Figure 2 from least to greatest.

9) Rank the resolution of the interferometers shown in Figure 2 from the smallest to the largest.

10) Match each of the four images of the sky in Figure 1 with the interferometer from Figure 2 that best matches the LCP and resolution of that image. Explain your reasoning.

You are in charge of a committee that assigns interferometer access to teams of astronomers. Currently there are four teams requesting access, and you have four interferometers available, so you need to choose which interferometer is most appropriate for each team. Each team wants to observe a different object in the sky, so they need different values for LCP and resolution. The table below contains information about the object that each of the four teams wants to observe. All teams will make observations at the <u>same wavelength</u>.

The figure below depicts the four interferometers that are currently available. Recall that the maximum baseline for an interferometer is the distance between the telescopes that are farthest apart.

Interferometer K

Interferometer L

Interferometer M

Interferometer N

Team	Object Observed	Object's Apparent Brightness	Resolution Required
1	Binary Star	Dim	Small
2	Star	Bright	Large
3	Galaxy	Bright	Moderate
4	Nebula	Dim	Moderate

11) State which of the four interferometers (K–N) you would assign to each of the four teams. Explain your reasoning.

Part I: Luminosity, Temperature, and Size

Imagine you are comparing the ability of electric hot plates of different sizes and temperatures to fully cook two identical large pots of spaghetti. Note that all the pots are as large as the largest hot plate. The shading of each hot plate is used to illustrate its temperature. The darker the shade of gray the cooler the temperature of the hot plate.

1) Four pairs of hot plates are shown below, A–D. For <u>each pair</u> of hot plates shown below, <u>circle the one</u> that will cook the large pot of spaghetti more quickly. <u>If there is no way to tell for sure,</u> state that explicitly.

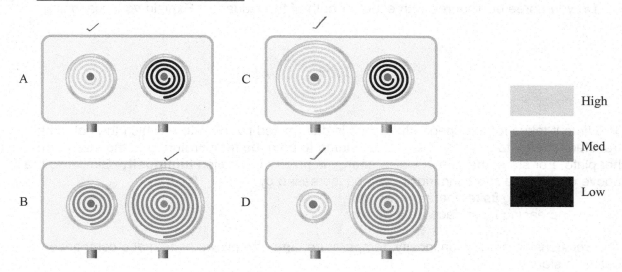

2) If you use two hot plates of the same size, can you assume that the hot plate that can cook a large pot of spaghetti first is at the higher temperature? Which lettered example above supports your answer?

yes, A

3) If you use two hot plates at the same temperature, can you assume that the hot plate that can cook a large pot of spaghetti first is larger? Which lettered example above supports your answer?

yes, B

4) If you use two hot plates of different sizes, can you assume that the hot plate that can cook a large pot of spaghetti first is at a higher temperature? Which lettered example above supports your answer?

yes, D

5) Two students are discussing their answers to Question 4:

Student 1: *In 1D, the hot plate on the left cooks the spaghetti quicker than the one on the right even though it is smaller. The hot plate's higher temperature is what makes it cook the spaghetti more quickly.*

Student 2: *But the size of the hot plate also plays a part in making it cook fast. If the hot plate on the left were the size of a penny, the spaghetti would take a really long time to cook. I bet that if the size difference were great enough, the one at the lower temperature could cook the spaghetti first.*

Do you agree or disagree with either or both of the students? Explain your reasoning.

Student 2

The time it takes for the spaghetti to cook is determined by the rate at which the hot plate transfers energy to the pot. This rate is related to both the temperature and the size of the hot plate. For stars, the rate at which energy is given off is called **luminosity.** Similar to the above example, a star's luminosity can be increased by
* increasing its temperature; and/or
* increasing its surface area (or size).

This relationship among luminosity, temperature, and size allows us to make comparisons between stars.

6) If two stars have the same surface temperature and one is more luminous, what can you conclude about the sizes of the stars?

different

7) If two stars have the same surface temperature and are the same size, which star, if either, is more luminous? Explain your reasoning.

Neither, they are the same

8) If two stars are the same size, but one has a higher surface temperature, which star, if either, is more luminous? Explain your reasoning.

The one with the higher surface temp

Part II: Application to the H–R Diagram

The graph below plots the luminosity of a star on the vertical axis against the star's surface temperature on the horizontal axis. This type of graph is called an H–R diagram. Use the H–R diagram below and the relationship between a star's luminosity, temperature, and size (as described on the previous page) to answer the following questions concerning the stars labeled U–Y. Note that the temperature on the H–R diagram increases from right to left.

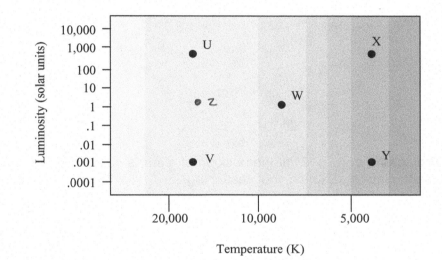

9) Stars U and V have the same surface temperature. Given that Star U is actually much more luminous than Star V, what can you conclude about the size of Star U compared to Star V? Explain your reasoning.

it must be larger

10) Star U has a greater surface temperature than Star X. Given that Star X is actually just as luminous as Star U, what can you conclude about the size of Star X compared to Star U? Explain your reasoning.

must be larger to close that gap

11) Based on the information presented in the H–R diagram, which star is larger, X or Y? Explain your reasoning.

X

12) Based on the information presented in the H–R diagram, which star is larger, Y or V? Explain your reasoning.

Y

13) On the H–R diagram, draw a "Z" at the position of a star smaller in size than Star W but with the same luminosity. Explain your reasoning.

14) It is very difficult to accurately predict how the size of Star U will compare to that of Star W (without performing some kind of calculation). Explain what makes a comparison of the size of these stars so difficult.

Because U is at a higher luminosity than W and has a higher temp so we know W is smaller but we don't know by how much

when temp or luminosity is held constant it is easy to estimate. to diff both is hard to compare size

Part I: Spectral Curves

A *spectral curve* (like the one shown below) is a graph that displays the amount of energy given off by an object each second versus the different wavelengths (or colors) of light. For a specific color of light on the horizontal axis, the height of the curve will indicate how much energy is being given off (each second) at that particular wavelength. Figure 1 shows the spectral curve for an object emitting more red and orange light than indigo and violet. Notice that the red end of the curve is higher than the violet end, so the object will appear slightly reddish in color.

1) At which color is the object in Figure 1 giving off the greatest amount of energy?

red

2) If the blue light and orange light coming from the object were blocked, then Figure 1 would have to be modified to look like which of the spectral curves shown below (a, b, or c)?

(A)

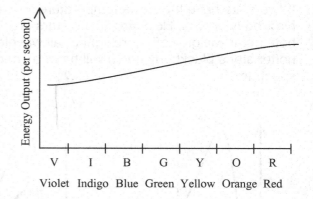

Violet Indigo Blue Green Yellow Orange Red

Figure 1

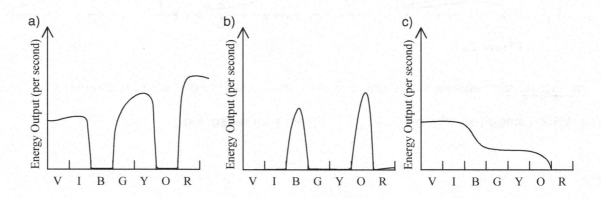

3) What colors of light are present in 2b above?

Blue and orange

4) What colors are present in 2c above? Would this object appear reddish or bluish?

everything except for red

bluish

Part II: Blackbody Curves

Figures 2a, 2b, and 2c display the blackbody curves for Stars C, D, E, and F. Two important features of a star's blackbody curve are:
- its maximum height or peak—where the energy output is greatest; and
- the corresponding <u>wavelength</u> at which this peak occurs—which is inversely related to the star's temperature. If the peak occurs at a long wavelength, the star is cool. If the peak occurs at a short wavelength the star will be hot.

If two stars have the same temperature and are the same size, they will have identical blackbody curves. However, if two stars are the same size, but one star is hotter, then the hotter star will give off more light at all wavelengths (a taller graph), and the peak of the hotter star's blackbody curve will be at a shorter wavelength (toward the blue end of the spectrum).

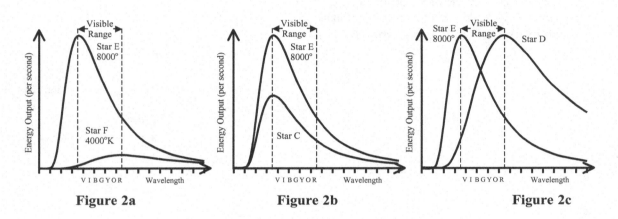

Figure 2a   **Figure 2b**   **Figure 2c**

<u>Use Figure 2a</u> to answer Questions 5–8. Assume Stars E and F are the same size.

5) Which star gives off more red light? Explain your reasoning.

6) Which star gives off more blue light? Explain your reasoning.

7) Which star looks redder? Explain your reasoning.

8) Two students are discussing their answers to Question 7.

Student 1: *Star E looks redder because it is giving off more red light than Star F.*

Student 2: *I disagree, you're ignoring how much blue light Star E gives off. Star E gives off more blue light than red light, so it looks bluish. Star F gives off more red than blue, so it looks reddish. That's why Star F looks redder than Star E.*

Do you agree or disagree with either or both of the students? Explain your reasoning.

↳ student 2

9) Using the blackbody curves shown in Figure 2b, for each characteristic listed in the table below circle the correct response in the column to the right.

Characteristic	Responses		
Peaks at a longer wavelength	Star E	Star C	They peak at the same wavelength
Has a lower surface temperature	Star E	Star C	They have the same surface temperature
Looks red	Star E	Star C	They both look red	Neither looks red
Looks blue	Star E	Star C	They both look blue	Neither looks blue
Has a greater energy output	Star E	Star C	The have the same energy output

10) How must Star C be different from Star E to account for their difference in energy output? Explain your reasoning.

→ size - star E is bigger

11) Two students are discussing their answers to Question 10.

Student 1: *The peaks are at the same place so they must be at the same temperature. If Star C were as big as Star E, it would have the same output. Since the output is lower, Star C must be smaller.*

Student 2: *I disagree, I think they could be the same size but the taller graph means Star E is hotter.*

Do you agree or disagree with either or both of the students? Explain your reasoning.

↳ student 1

Consider the blackbody curves for Stars E and D shown in Figure 2c when answering Questions 12–14.

12) For each star, describe its color as either reddish or bluish.

Star E: bluish   Star D: reddish

13) Which star has the greater surface temperature? Explain your reasoning.

Star E

14) Which star is larger? Explain your reasoning. (Hint: Consider how the energy output and temperatures for the two stars compare.)

D   make up difference in temp to give them the same energy output

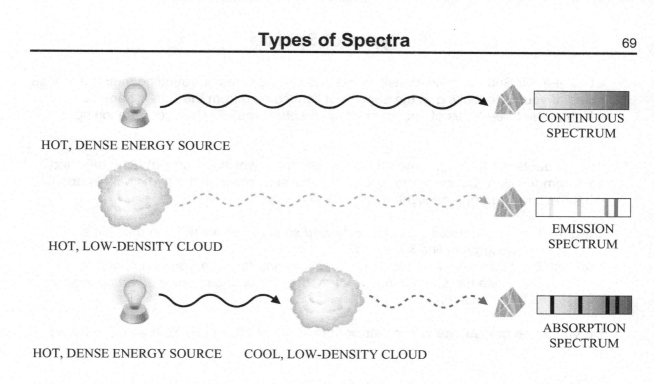

HOT, DENSE ENERGY SOURCE

CONTINUOUS SPECTRUM

HOT, LOW-DENSITY CLOUD

EMISSION SPECTRUM

HOT, DENSE ENERGY SOURCE COOL, LOW-DENSITY CLOUD

ABSORPTION SPECTRUM

1) What type of spectrum is produced when the light emitted directly from a hot, dense object passes through a prism?

continuous

2) What type of spectrum is produced when the light emitted directly from a hot, low-density cloud of gas passes through a prism?

emission

3) Describe in detail the source of light and the path the light must take to produce an absorption spectrum.

the source has to be hot + dense + must take a path through a cool less dense cloud

4) There are dark lines in the absorption spectrum that represent missing light. What happened to this light that is missing in the absorption line spectrum?

absorbed by cool & low dense cloud

5) Stars like our Sun have low-density, gaseous atmospheres surrounding their hot, dense cores. If you were looking at the spectra of light coming from the Sun (or any star), which of the three types of spectrum would be observed? Explain your reasoning.

continuous - nothing in the way   absorption if cool low
emission - low density cloud in path   density cloud

6) Two students are looking at the brightly lit full Moon, which is illuminated by reflected light from the Sun. Consider the following discussion between the two students about what the spectrum of moonlight would look like.

Student 1: *I think moonlight is just reflected sunlight, so we will see the Sun's absorption line spectrum.*

Student 2: *I disagree. An absorption spectrum has to come from a hot, dense object. Since the Moon is not a hot, dense object, it can't give off an absorption line spectrum.*

Do you agree or disagree with either or both of the students? Explain your reasoning.

↳student 1

7) Imagine that you are looking at two different spectra of the Sun. Spectrum #1 is obtained using a telescope that is in a high orbit far above Earth's atmosphere. Spectrum #2 is obtained using a telescope located on the surface of Earth. Label each spectrum below as either Spectrum #1 or Spectrum #2.

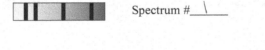   Spectrum #__1__

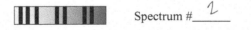   Spectrum #__2__

Explain the reasoning behind your choices.

low density cloud of atmosphere
absorbs more of the light
given by sun and therefore
we will see more wavelengths
absorbed

In this activity, we will use a representation of the atom in which a central nucleus containing the protons and neutrons is surrounded by circles that represent the energy levels electrons can occupy.

1) Draw an atom including a nucleus and five energy levels that electrons could occupy. Use a dot to represent an electron at the lowest energy level.

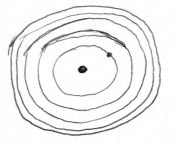

One way an atom emits light (photons) occurs when an electron drops down from a higher energy level (also referred to as an excited state) to a lower energy level (the lowest energy level is referred to as the ground state).

2) Will an atom emit light if all of the atom's electrons are in the ground state? Explain your reasoning.

No, because if electrons are not able to go lower in energy & therefore can't emit light

3) In which case does an atom emit more energy (*circle one*)?

Case A: *An electron drops down from the first excited state to the ground state.*
Case B: *An electron drops down from the third excited state to the ground state.*

Explain your reasoning.

B, dropping same as A and additional levels

4) Two students are talking about how light is emitted from atoms. Consider the following discussion between the two students and the sketches each student drew to illustrate their thinking.

Student 1:   *I drew my atom like this because our professor said that the gap between the energy levels gets bigger and bigger as you go up in energy from the ground state.*

Student 2:   *I think you've got it backward. The gap between energy levels will get smaller as you go up in energy levels, like I've drawn.*

Student 1 Drawing   Student 2 Drawing

Do you agree or disagree with either or both of the students? Explain your reasoning, and describe how you could change your drawing from Question 1 to make it more accurate.

5) Stars like our Sun have low-density, gaseous atmospheres surrounding their hot, dense cores. If you were looking at the spectra of light coming from the Sun (or any star), which type of spectrum would be observed?

continuous spectrum   absorption spectrum   emission spectrum

6) At the right is a sketch showing one of the atoms in the cool cloud of gas described in the previous question. Using a dot to represent an electron, a straight arrow to represent the motion of the electron between energy levels, and a squiggly arrow to represent the photon, sketch what you think would happen within this atom to cause the type of spectrum described in the previous question. Explain the reasoning behind why you drew the electron and arrows the way you did.

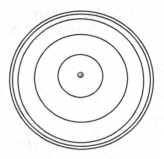

7) Imagine that you are looking at a neon sign in a store window that says "OPEN." This sign can be thought of as a tube filled with a gas of neon atoms that have electrons changing from one energy state to a different energy state and in the process are giving off mostly red light. Which type of spectrum would you observe coming from the "OPEN" sign (*circle one*)?

continuous spectrum   absorption spectrum   emission spectrum

Explain the reasoning behind your choice.

8) At the right is a sketch showing one of the atoms in the neon sign described in the previous question. Using a dot to represent an electron, a straight arrow to represent the motion of the electron between energy levels, and a squiggly arrow to represent the photon, sketch what you think would happen within this atom to cause the type of spectrum described in the previous question. Explain the reasoning behind why you drew the electron and arrows the way you did.

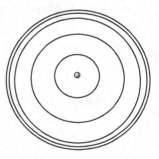

11) Use the hypothetical atom drawings (A–E) below to answer the next five questions. Note there is only one correct choice for each question and each choice is used only once.

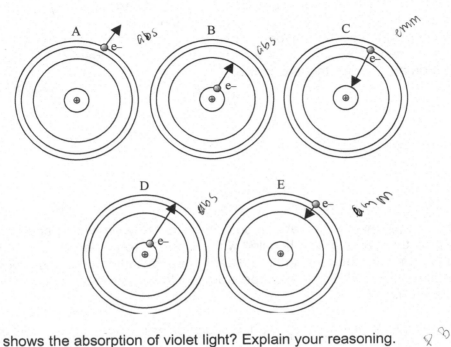

a) Which shows the absorption of violet light? Explain your reasoning.

b) Which shows the emission of blue light? Explain your reasoning.

c) Which shows the absorption of green light? Explain your reasoning.

d) Which shows the emission of orange light? Explain your reasoning.

e) Which shows an electron being ejected from the atom?

Part I: Light and Molecules

A molecule can change its vibrational energy state by emitting or absorbing an <u>infrared</u> wavelength photon. In each of the four cases shown below (A–D), a molecule is shown transitioning between two different energy states depending on whether the molecule absorbed or emitted a photon.

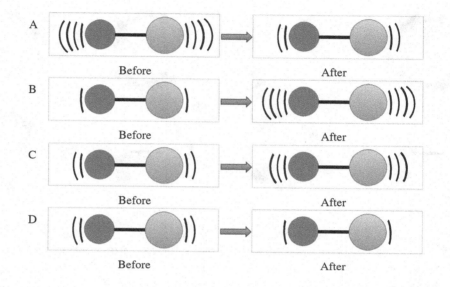

1) Which of the cases (A–D) shown above correspond with the absorption of light, and which correspond with the emission of light? Draw in a squiggly arrow going into or out of the molecule to represent the aborption or emission of a photon for each case (A–D).

2) In which case was a photon with the longest wavelength absorbed? Explain your reasoning.

3) In which case was a photon with the greatest energy emitted? Explain your reasoning.

Observing the Invisible—Molecular Excitations and Synchrotron Radiation

A molecule can change its rotational energy state by emitting or absorbing a <u>radio</u> wavelength photon. In each of the four cases shown below (A–D), a molecule is shown transitioning between two different energy states depending on whether the molecule absorbed or emitted a photon.

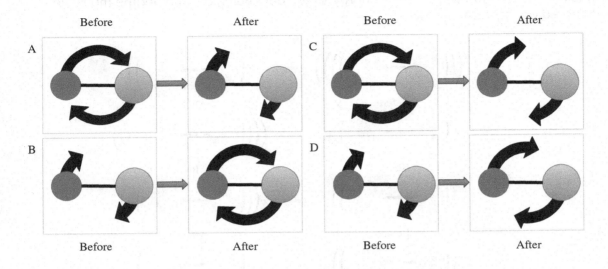

4) Which of the cases (A–D) shown above correspond with the absorption of light, and which correspond with the emission of light? Draw in a squiggly arrow going into or out of the molecule to represent the aborption or emission of a photon for each case (A–D).

5) In which case was a photon with the shortest wavelength emitted? Explain your reasoning.

6) In which case was a photon with the least energy is absorbed? Explain your reasoning.

7) Circle the correct type of light (from those listed in parentheses) to complete the sentences in the following paragraph.

Because only a small amount of energy is needed to change a molecule's rotational energy state, the emission and absorption lines for rotating molecules are typically at _____ (radio / infrared / visible) wavelengths. Making a molecule change vibrational energy states requires a little more energy, so the emission and absorption lines for vibrating molecules are typically at _____ (radio / infrared / visible) wavelengths. Making an electron change orbital energy levels in an atom requires even more energy, so the emission and absorption lines for electron transitions are typically found at _____ (radio / infrared / visible) wavelengths.

Part II: Synchrotron Radiation

The drawing below shows the light emitted when a charged particle (e.g., an electron or a proton) is spiraling around a magnetic field. The charged particle experiences an acceleration as it spirals and this acceleration causes light to be emitted. We call the light that is emitted by this process as **synchrotron radiation**.

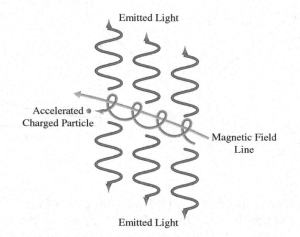

The graph below shows the amount of energy emitted each second over all wavelengths of light, for an object emitting synchrotron radiation.

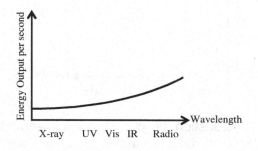

8) At which wavelength(s) does synchrotron radiation emit light?

9) At which wavelength does synchrotron radiation emit the most energy per second?

10) Is it possible to detect synchrotron radiation with an X-ray telescope? Explain your reasoning.

The figure below shows a pulsar, which is the remnant of a dead massive star. A pulsar has a strong magnetic field, around which jets of charged particles spiral, producing synchrotron radiation. The hot surface of a pulsar produces thermal radiation with a spectrum that peaks in X-rays.

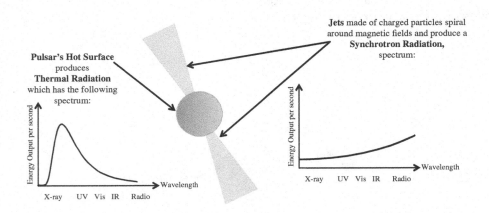

11) Imagine you could observe the pulsar at all wavelengths of light, from X-rays to radio. On the graph below, sketch the spectrum of light you would detect that results from the **combination** of the synchrotron radiation from the pulsar's jets and the thermal radiation from the pulsar's surface.

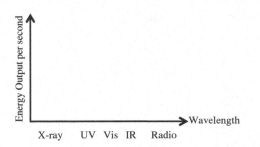

12) On the graph you made in Question 11, <u>circle</u> the wavelengths at which you receive more light from the synchrotron radiation from the pulsar's jets than thermal radiation from the pulsar's surface. Put a <u>box</u> around the wavelengths at which you receive more light from the thermal radiation from the pulsar's surface than synchrotron radiation from the pulsar's jets.

13) Which one type of light is best for observing the pulsar's synchrotron radiation? Explain your reasoning.

Part III: Real Telescopes and Observations

Here are four real telescopes:
- The Atacama Large Millimeter Array (ALMA) is a radio telescope located in Chile
- The Chandra X-ray Observatory is an X-ray telescope located in space, orbiting the Earth
- The Spitzer Space Telescope is an IR telescope located in space, orbiting the Sun
- The Galaxy Evolution Explorer (GALEX) is a UV telescope located in space, orbiting the Earth

Use the above information to help answer the following questions.

14) Astronomers, trying to understand the origins of life, observe rotating organic molecules in nebulae. Which telescope listed above would be best to detect the light from these organic molecules in nebulae? Explain your reasoning.

15) Consider the spectrum of light shown below.

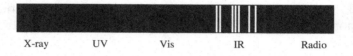

X-ray   UV   Vis   IR   Radio

a) This spectrum is produced by _____ (circle one of the following five choices).
- the hot surface of a pulsar
- charged particles spiraling around a magnetic field
- electrons changing energy states
- molecules changing vibrational states
- molecules changing rotational states

b) Which telescope listed above would you use to detect this spectrum? Explain your reasoning.

16) Black holes have extremely large magnetic fields that cause charged particles to accelerate away from the black hole, creating jets of material. The charged particles spiral around the magnetic field and emit light as they are ejected. Is it *possible* for an astronomer to detect the light from a black hole jet if he or she uses the Chandra X-ray Observatory? Explain your reasoning.

A molecule changes its vibrational energy state as shown in the figure below.

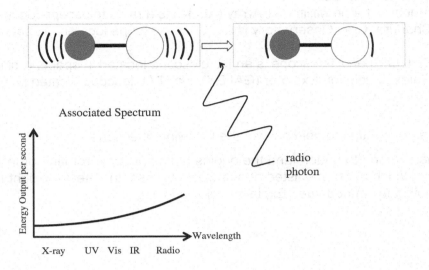

17) Which of the following are represented incorrectly: the direction of the photon, the energy of the photon, and/or the associated spectrum of light? Explain your reasoning.

18) Correct the graphs and drawings in Question 17 to fix all of the errors you identified with the direction of the photon, the energy of the photon, and/or the associated spectrum of light.

The absorption line spectra for six hypothetical stars, each with different temperatures, are shown below. For each absorption line spectrum, the short wavelengths of light (or blue end) of the electromagnetic spectrum are shown on the left side, and the long wavelengths of light (or red end) of the spectrum are shown on the right side.

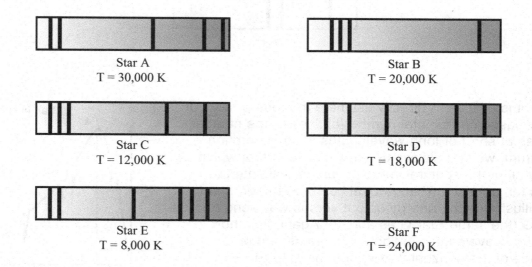

Star A
T = 30,000 K

Star B
T = 20,000 K

Star C
T = 12,000 K

Star D
T = 18,000 K

Star E
T = 8,000 K

Star F
T = 24,000 K

1) Do the cooler stars appear to have a different (greater or fewer) number of lines in their absorption spectra than hotter stars? Cite evidence from the above spectra to support your answer.

2) Do cooler stars appear to have more lines at either the blue or red ends of their absorption spectra than hotter stars? Cite evidence from the above spectra to support your answer.

3) Consider the following statement made by a student regarding a star's temperature and its corresponding absorption line spectrum.

Student: *If I am looking at a star's absorption line spectrum and see that it has a lot of lines at the blue end of the spectrum, then the star must be hot because the blue lines are higher energy lines.*

Do you agree or disagree with this student? Explain your reasoning and support your answer by citing evidence from the absorption line spectra given for Stars A–F.

4) Consider the absorption line spectrum given below for Star G. Can you determine the approximate temperature for Star G by comparing its absorption line spectrum to the absorption line spectra and temperatures of Stars A–F given above? If so, write in your estimate in the space below; if not, explain why not.

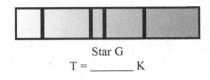

Star G

T = _____ K

While it is difficult to directly estimate the temperature of a star based on the total number of lines or the number of lines at short or long wavelengths in its absorption spectrum, we can always use the wavelength at which the peak of the spectral curve occurs to estimate the star's temperature. The spectral curve on the graph at right illustrates the energy output versus wavelength for Star G (the same Star G as above). Again, the short (or blue) wavelengths of light are represented on the left side of the horizontal axis, and the long (or red) wavelengths of light are represented on the right end of the horizontal axis.

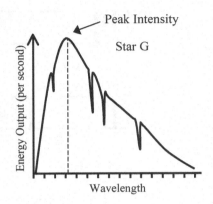

There are two important features represented on this spectral curve that you need to consider.
- The exact locations of the small dips, or absorption features, on the curve occur at the same wavelength as the dark lines that appear in the absorption line spectrum shown on the previous page.
- The wavelength at which the object's peak energy output occurs is directly related to the object's temperature. Hotter objects have their peak energy output occur at short wavelengths—toward the blue end of the spectrum. Cooler objects have their peak energy output occur at long wavelengths—toward the red end of the spectrum.

Although the total energy output of a star is affected by its temperature (and, therefore, so is the height of the spectral curve), for this activity, we will assume that the height (but not location) of the peak energy output, and the general shape of the spectral curves for Stars A–F, can be drawn nearly the same for each star. Only the wavelength of the spectral curve's peak and the location of the small dips, or absorption features, will be different for each star.

5) Examine the spectral curve shown at right for Star A (the same Star A as on the previous page). Note that Star G has a temperature of approximately 25,000 K, whereas Star A has a temperature of 30,000 K. Based on this information, is the wavelength of the peak of the spectral curve for Star A drawn correctly when compared to the wavelength of the peak for Star G? Explain your reasoning.

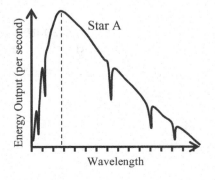

6) Are the absorption features (dips) in the spectral curve for Star A drawn at approximately the correct wavelengths? Explain how you can tell.

7) Sketch spectral curves for Stars B–F on the corresponding graphs provided below. Do not worry about whether the heights of the spectral curves you draw are accurate. However, make sure the wavelength of the peak and the absorption dips are drawn at (approximately) the correct wavelengths.

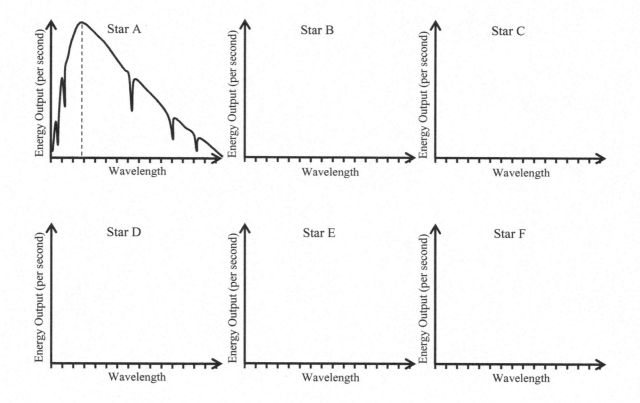

8) Did you draw the peak of each spectral curve at the same wavelength as the spectral curve for Star A? Why or why not?

9) If you were given a star's absorption line spectrum and its corresponding spectral curve shown on an energy output per second versus wavelength graph, how could you approximate the temperature of the star?

Part I: Motion of Source

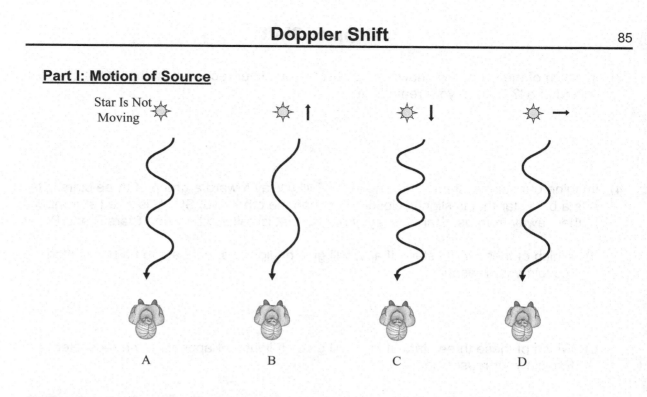

Star Is Not Moving

A   B   C   D

1) For the situations (A–D) shown above, consider only the instant shown (not what the star was doing just before or after the instant shown).

   a) In which situation will the observer receive light that is shifted to shorter wavelengths?

   C

   b) Will this light be blueshifted or redshifted for this case?

   c) What direction is the star moving relative to the observer for this case?

   toward them

2) Consider the situations shown (A–D).

   a) In which situation will the observer receive light that is shifted to longer wavelengths?

   B

   b) Will this light be blueshifted or redshifted for this case?

   c) What direction is the star moving relative to the observer for this case?

   away from the observer

3) In which of the situations shown (A–D) will the observer receive light that is not Doppler shifted at all? Explain your reasoning.

D, it is being shifted side to side

A, not moving at all

4) Imagine our solar system is moving in the Milky Way toward a group of three stars. Star A is a blue star that is slightly closer to us than the other two. Star B is a red star that is farthest away from us. Star C is a yellow star that is halfway between Stars A and B.

a) Which of these three stars, if any, will give off light that appears to be blueshifted? Explain your reasoning.

all 3 they are all moving toward us

b) Which of these three stars, if any, will give off light that appears to be redshifted? Explain your reasoning.

None, same reason as above

c) Which of these three stars, if any, will give off light that appears to have no shift? Explain your reasoning.

None, same reasoning

5) You overhear two students discussing the topic of Doppler shift.

Student 1:   *Since Betelgeuse is a red star, it must be going away from us, and since Rigel is a blue star it must be coming toward us.*

Student 2:   *I disagree, the color of the star does not tell you if it is moving. You have to look at the shift in wavelength of the lines in the star's absorption spectrum to determine whether it's moving toward or away from you.*

Do you agree or disagree with either or both of the students? Explain your reasoning.

↳ student 2

Part II: Shift in Absorption Spectra

When we study an astronomical object like a star or galaxy, we examine the spectrum of light it gives off. Since the lines of a spectrum occur at specific wavelengths, we can determine that an object is moving when we see that the lines have been shifted to either longer or shorter wavelengths. For the absorption line spectra shown on the next page, short-wavelength light (the blue end of the spectrum) is shown on the left-hand side, and long-wavelength light (the red end of the spectrum) is shown on the right-hand side.

For the three absorption line spectra shown below (A, B, and C), one of the spectra corresponds to a star that is <u>not moving</u> relative to you, one of the spectra is from a star that is moving <u>toward</u> you, and one of the spectra is from a star that is moving <u>away</u> from you.

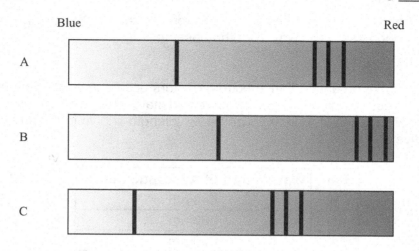

6) Which of the three spectra above corresponds with the star moving toward you? Explain your reasoning.

C, because A isn't moving its the middle of the s
C is blueshift because wavelength are
to the blue side of spectrum which means
it needs to be moving toward you.

7) Which of the three spectra corresponds with the star moving away from you? Explain your reasoning.

B, same but opposite reasoning
as above
redshifted → away from you

Part III: Size of Shift and Speed

If two sources of light are moving relative to an observer, the light from the star that is moving faster will appear to undergo a greater Doppler shift.

Consider the four spectra at the right. The spectrum labeled F is an absorption line spectrum from a star that is <u>at rest</u>. Again, note that short-wavelength (blue) light is shown on the left-hand side of each spectrum, and long-wavelength (red) light is shown on the right-hand side of each spectrum.

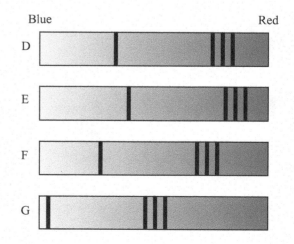

8) Which of the four spectra is from the star that is moving the fastest? Is this star moving toward or away from the observer?

    G, toward

9) Of the stars that are moving, which spectra is from the star that is moving the slowest? Is this star moving toward or away from the observer?

    D, away

10) An important line in the absorption spectrum of stars occurs at a wavelength of 656 nm for stars at rest. Imagine that you observe five stars (H–L) and discover that this important absorption line is measured at the wavelength shown in the table below for each of the five stars.

    B ← 656 → R

Star	Wavelength of Absorption Line
H	649 nm 7
I	660 nm 4
J	656 nm
K	658 nm 2
L	647 nm 9

a) Which of the stars are giving off light that appears blueshifted? Explain your reasoning.

    H, L

b) Which of the stars are giving off light that appears redshifted? Explain your reasoning.

    K, I

c) Which star is moving the fastest? Is it moving toward or away from the observer? Explain your reasoning.

    L, biggest distance

d) Which of the stars (H–L) would appear blue? Which of the stars (H–L) would appear red? Explain your reasoning. If you (cannot determine) which star (H–L) would appear red or blue, explain why not.

> Distance doesn't affect color of star

e) Which of the stars (H–L) is closest to Earth? Which of the stars (H–L) is farthest from Earth? Explain your reasoning. If you cannot determine which star (H–L) is closest or furthest from Earth, explain why not.

> L most blueshifted, moving toward us

11) The figure at right shows a spaceprobe and five planets (A–E). The motion of the spaceprobe is indicated by the arrow. The spaceprobe is continuously broadcasting a radio signal in all directions. Answer Questions a–e for the spaceprobe at the location shown.

a) Will all the planets receive radio signals from the spaceprobe that are Doppler shifted? Explain your reasoning.

> No moving to the side
> for planets C & D
> so no-doppler shift

A

C   D

b) Which planets will receive a radio signal that is shifted to shorter wavelengths? Explain your reasoning.   B

> B, E moves toward them
> which is blueshifted
> or shorter wavelengths

B

E

c) Which planets will receive a radio signal that is redshifted? Explain your reasoning.

not to scale

> A, moving away from it

d) How will the size of the Doppler shift in the radio signals detected at Planets A and B compare? Explain your reasoning.

Shifts for A and B will be the
same but in differend direction

e) How will the size of the Doppler shift in the radio signals detected at Planets E and B compare? Explain your reasoning.

Same shift because distance from
object does not matter the only
thing that matters is how fast it is moving

Figure 1 shows Earth, the Sun, and five different possible positions for the Moon during one full orbit (dotted line). It is important to recall that one-half of the Moon's surface is illuminated by sunlight at all times. For each of the five positions of the Moon shown below, the Moon has been shaded on one side to indicate the half of the Moon's surface that is **not** being illuminated by sunlight. Note that this drawing is not to scale.

1) Which Moon position (A–E) best corresponds with the Moon phase shown in the upper-right corner of Figure 1? Make sure that the Moon position you choose correctly predicts a Moon phase in which only a small crescent of light on the left-hand side of the Moon is visible from Earth.

   Enter the letter of your choice: __D__

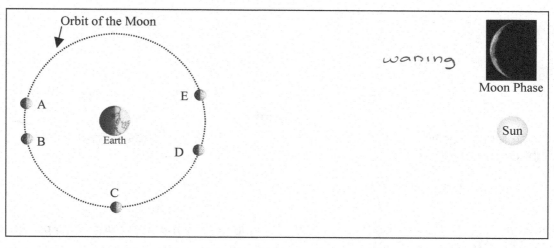

Figure 1

2) In the blank boxes below, sketch how the Moon would appear from Earth for the four Moon positions that you did **not** choose in Question 1. Be sure to label each sketch with the corresponding letter indicating the Moon's position from Figure 1.

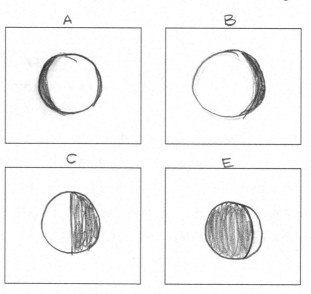

3) Shade in each of the four Moons shown in Figure 2 to indicate which portion of the Moon's surface will **not** be illuminated by sunlight.

Use Figure 2 to answer Questions 4–7.

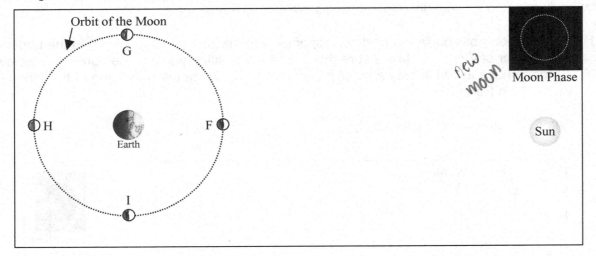

Figure 2

4) Which Moon position (F–I) best corresponds with the Moon phase shown in the upper-right corner of Figure 2?

Enter the letter of your choice: ____F____

5) How much of the entire Moon's surface is illuminated by the Sun during this phase (*circle one*)?

   a) None of the surface is illuminated.

   b) Less than half of the surface is illuminated.

   c) Half of the surface is illuminated.

   d) More than half of the surface is illuminated.

   e) All of the surface is illuminated.

6) How much of the Moon's illuminated surface is visible from Earth for this phase of the Moon (*circle one*)?

   a) None of the Moon's illuminated surface is visible from Earth.

   b) Less than half of the Moon's illuminated surface is visible from Earth.

   c) Half of the Moon's illuminated surface is visible from Earth.

   d) More than half of the Moon's illuminated surface is visible from Earth.

   e) All of the Moon's illuminated surface is visible from Earth.

7) Would your answers to Questions 5 or 6 change if the Moon were in the third-quarter phase rather than the phase shown in Figure 2? Explain your reasoning.

yes because the moon would be in a different orbital position to the earth so we will see a different position and portion of illuminated light

8) Consider the following discussion between two students about the cause of the phases of the Moon.

Student 1: *The phase of the Moon depends on how the Moon, Sun, and Earth are aligned with one another.* T *During some alignments only a small portion of the Moon's surface will receive light from the Sun, in which case we would see a crescent Moon.* F

Student 2: *I disagree. The Moon would always get the same amount of sunlight;* T *it's just that in some alignments Earth casts a larger shadow on the Moon. That's why the Moon isn't always a full Moon.* F

Do you agree or disagree with either or both of the students? Explain your reasoning.

I agree w/ student 2 because the sun is always illuminating 1/2 of the moon. Therefore ~~our position and~~ the moons place in its orbit will play a role on how much we will see of the illuminated half.

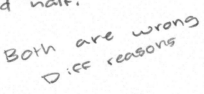

Both are wrong
Diff reasons

1) If the Moon is a full Moon tonight, will the Moon be waxing or waning one week later? Which side of the Moon (right or left) will appear illuminated at this time?

   Circle one: Waxing or (Waning)

   Circle one: Right or (Left)

2) Where (in the southern sky, on the eastern horizon, on the western horizon, high in the sky, etc.) would you look to see the full Moon when it starts to rise? What time would this happen?   western , 6pm

3) Where (in the southern sky, on the eastern horizon, on the western horizon, high in the sky, etc.) would you look to see the Sun when the full Moon starts to rise?

4) Where (in the southern sky, on the eastern horizon, on the western horizon, high in the sky, etc.) would you look to see the new Moon, if it were visible, when it starts to rise? What time would this happen?

5) If the Moon is a new Moon when it rises, which of the phases shown below (A–H) will it be in when it sets?

   Letter of Moon phase: ___A___

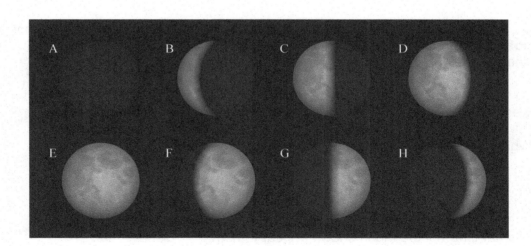

Figure 1 shows the position of the Sun, Earth, and Moon for a particular phase of the Moon. The Moon has been shaded on one side to indicate the portion of the Moon that is **not** being illuminated by sunlight. A person has been placed on Earth to indicate an observer's position at noon. Recall that with this representation Earth will complete one counterclockwise rotation in each day. Note that this drawing is not to scale.

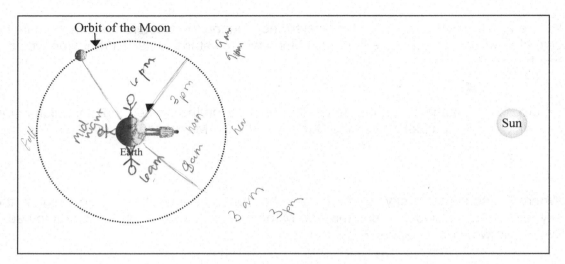

Figure 1

6) What time is it for the person shown in Figure 1?

   Circle one: 6 A.M. (sunrise)   (12 P.M. (noon))   6 P.M. (sunset)   12 A.M. (midnight)

7) Draw a stick figure of a person on Earth in Figure 1 for each of the three times that you did **not** choose in Question 6. Label each of the stick figures that you drew with the time that the person would be located there.

8) Answer the following questions for the position of the Moon shown in Figure 1.

   a) Which Moon phase would an Earth observer see?   *waxing gibbous*

   b) At what time will the Moon shown appear highest in the sky?   *9pm*

   c) At what time will the Moon shown appear to rise?   *3pm*

   d) At what time will the Moon shown appear to set?   *3 am*

9) At what time would you look to see a first-quarter Moon at its highest position in the sky?

Sunset or 6pm

10) If the Sun set below your western horizon about 2 hours ago, and the Moon is barely visible on the eastern horizon, what phase would the Moon be in at this time and location?

8pm

2am highest

8pm

waning gibbous

11) A friend comments to you that there was a beautiful, thin sliver of Moon visible in the early morning just before sunrise. Which phase of the Moon would this be, and in what direction would you look to see the Moon (in the southern sky, on the eastern horizon, on the western horizon, high in the sky, etc.)?

waning cressent

rising time -> on eastern horizon

Figure1 illustrates the sky as seen from the continental United States. It shows that the Sun's daily path across the sky (dashed/solid line) is longest on June 21 and shortest on December 21. In addition, on June 21, which is called the summer solstice, the Sun reaches its maximum height in the southern sky above the horizon at about noon. The figure shows that the Sun never actually reaches the zenith for any observer in the continental United States. In other words, the Sun is never directly overhead. Over the six months following the summer solstice, the height of the Sun at noon moves progressively lower and lower until December 21, the winter solstice. Thus, we see that the path of the Sun through the southern sky changes considerably over the course of a year.

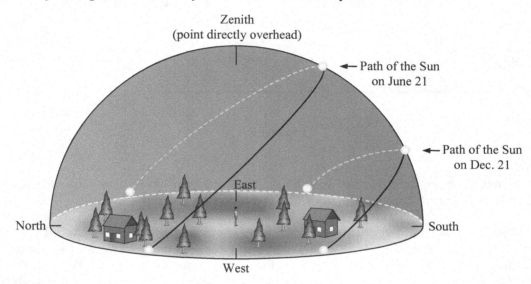

Figure 1

1) According to Figure 1, in which direction would you look to see the Sun when it reaches its highest position in the sky today?

   Circle one: east   southeast   south   southwest   west

2) If it is wintertime right now (just after the winter solstice), how does the height of the Sun at noon change over the next several months?

   Circle one: increases   stays the same   decreases

3) Is there ever a time of year when the Sun is directly overhead at the zenith at noon for an observer in the continental United States? If so, on what date does this occur?

4) During which month(s) of the year would the Sun rise:

   a) north of east?

   b) south of east?

   c) directly in the east?

5) Does the Sun always set in precisely the same location on the horizon throughout the year? If not, describe how the direction that the Sun sets on the horizon changes throughout the year.

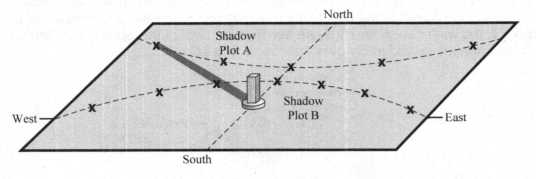

Figure 2

Figure 2 shows a small, vertical stick, which casts a shadow while it rests on a large piece of paper or poster board. You can think of this to be somewhat like a sundial.

For two different days of the year, the end of the stick's shadow has been marked with an **x** every couple of hours throughout the day. Although this sketch is somewhat exaggerated, these *shadow plots* indicate how the position of the Sun changes in the sky through the course of these two days. The following questions are designed to show the relationship between Figure 1 on the previous page and Figure 2 above.

6) What do the **x**'s in the shadow plots represent?

7) Approximately how much time went by from the time one of the **x**'s was drawn until the next **x** was drawn for each shadow plot?

8) Approximately how long did it take to create each of the shadow plots?

9) How does the direction of the stick's shadow compare to the direction of the Sun at the time each **x** was drawn?

10) Using Figures 1 and 2, in what direction would the shadow of the stick be cast on the poster board if the Sun rises in the southeast?

   Circle one: west   northwest   north   northeast   east   southeast

11) Clearly circle the **x** for the shadow that corresponds to noon for Shadow Plot A and for Shadow Plot B.

12) Which Shadow Plot (A or B) corresponds to the path of the Sun in which the Sun is highest in the sky at noon? Explain your reasoning.

13) Which Shadow Plot (A or B) most closely corresponds to the Sun's path through the sky during the summer, and which corresponds with the winter? Label these paths on Figure 2. Explain your reasoning.

14) On Figure 2, sketch a small Sun on the paper to indicate where on the horizon the Sun would be soon after sunrise in the summer and label the **x** that indicates the position of the stick's shadow at this time. Explain your reasoning for why you sketched the Sun where you did and labeled the **x** that you did.

15) Based on the shadow plots in Figure 2, during which time of the year (summer or winter) does the Sun rise to the south of east? Explain your reasoning.

16) Imagine Shadow Plot A corresponds to the path of the Sun on the winter solstice. Will there ever be a day when the stick's shadow at noon is longer than the one shown on Shadow Plot A at noon? Explain your reasoning.

17) Imagine Shadow Plot B corresponds to the path of the Sun on the summer solstice. Will there ever be a day when the stick's shadow at noon is shorter than the one shown on Shadow Plot B at noon? Explain your reasoning.

18) If you were to mark the top of the stick's shadow with an **x**, where would the **x** be placed along the north-to-south line to indicate the Sun's position at noon *today*? Clearly explain why you placed the **x** where you did.

19) Will the stick ever cast a shadow along the north-to-south line that extends to the south of the stick at noon? Explain your reasoning.

20) Is there ever a clear (no clouds) day of the year in the continental United States when the stick casts no shadow? If so, when does this occur, and where exactly in the sky does the Sun have to be?

Part I: Earth–Sun Distance

Listed below are the distances, in kilometers (km), between the Sun and Earth for four months of the year. The drawing at the right shows four different locations of Earth during its orbit around the Sun. Note that for each location drawn, Earth is correctly shown with its rotational axis tilted at an angle of 23.5°.

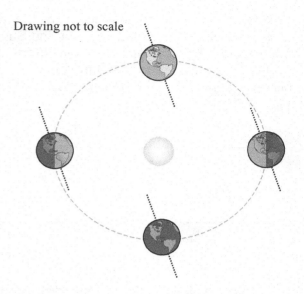

Drawing not to scale

Month	Earth–Sun Distance
December	147.2 million km
June	152.0 million km
September	150.2 million km
March	149.0 million km

1) Is the direction that Earth's axis is tilted changing as Earth orbits the Sun?

2) Using the information listed above, does Earth stay the same distance from the Sun throughout the year? If not, what month(s) and during which season (for the Northern Hemisphere) is Earth closest to the Sun? Farthest from the Sun?

3) Would you say the temperature stays approximately the same every month of the year at your location?

4) Are the seasons (summer or winter) the same in the Northern and Southern Hemispheres at the same time? When it is summer in the Northern Hemisphere, what season is it in the Southern Hemisphere?

5) Consider the following discussion between two students about the cause of the seasons.

   Student 1: *I know that it's hotter in the summer and colder in the winter, so we must be closer to the Sun in the summer than in the winter.*

   Student 2: *I disagree. Although the distance between Earth and the Sun does change throughout the year, I don't believe that the seasons and changes in Earth's surface temperature are caused by the distance between the Sun and Earth. If the seasons were due to the Sun–Earth distance, then both hemispheres of Earth would have the same seasons at the same time.*

   Do you agree or disagree with either or both of the students? Explain your reasoning.

At different times of the year, locations in the Northern Hemisphere can be a few thousand kilometers closer to (or farther from) the Sun than locations that are at the same latitude in the Southern Hemisphere (as shown in the drawing below). However, the distance between Earth and the Sun (about 150 million kilometers) is much greater than this difference in distance between the Earth's hemispheres and the Sun.

Northern Hemisphere Location

Sun

Drawing not to scale

Southern Hemisphere Location

6) Do you think the differences in distance between Earth's Northern and Southern Hemispheres are the cause of the seasons? Explain your reasoning.

7) Consider the following discussion between two students about the cause of the seasons.

Student 1: *I get it. So since Earth is tilted, there are times when the northern part of Earth is closer to the Sun than the southern part. So the north has summer and the south has winter. And then later, the south is tilted toward the Sun and gets closer and has summer.*

Student 2: *I disagree. Although the tilt does bring one hemisphere a little bit closer to the Sun, the difference in distance between the northern half and southern half of Earth is really small compared to the distance between Earth and the Sun.*

Do you agree or disagree with either or both of the students? Explain your reasoning.

Part II: Direct Light and Tilt

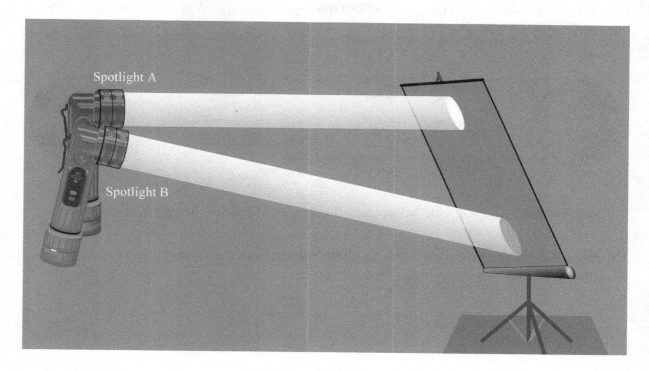

Consider the picture above in which two Spotlights (A and B) are shown casting light onto a screen. Note: Each spotlight gives off the same total amount of light.

8) Which of the two lighted areas (the one created by Spotlight A or B) is brighter?

9) Which of the two lighted areas is smaller?

10) Which of the two lighted areas receives more direct light (a greater amount of energy on each unit of area) from the spotlight?

11) If a thermometer were placed in each of the lighted areas, which one would read the higher temperature?

12) Which of the two positions would be similar to the way the sunlight would shine on the Northern Hemisphere of Earth during summer in the Northern Hemisphere? Explain your reasoning.

Consider the picture below illustrating three different regions of Earth (the Northern Hemisphere, the Southern Hemisphere, and the equatorial region) at two different times of the year, six months apart.

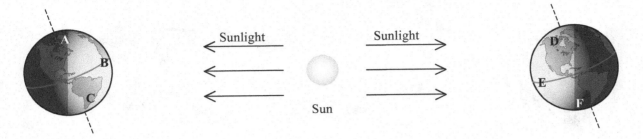

Note: this drawing is not to scale. In fact you could fit more than 100 Suns between the Sun and Earth.

13) Which location(s) (A–F) are in the Northern Hemisphere during summer? Explain your reasoning.

14) Which location(s) (A–F) are in the Southern Hemisphere during winter? Explain your reasoning.

Part III: Amount of Daylight

15) During which season (summer or winter) is the number of daylight hours the greatest? How many hours?

16) During which season (summer or winter) is the Sun highest in the sky at noon? Hint: Consider the drawing showing the lighted areas and the spotlights for Questions 7–11.

17) How are your answers to the previous two questions related to the time of year that your location experiences the highest average temperature? Explain your reasoning.

IV: Putting It All Together

18) Provide two pieces of evidence to support the fact that the varying distance between the Sun and Earth cannot account for the seasons.

19) Complete the sentences below by using the words provided in the parentheses ().

When it is summer, the tilt of the Earth causes the Sun to be above the horizon for _____ (many, few) hours of the day, and the Sun at noon will be _____ (high, low) in the sky, providing _____ (direct, indirect) sunlight to that hemisphere of the Earth.

One of the most difficult parts of constructing an accurate model for planetary motions is that planets seem to wander among the stars. During their normal (or prograde) motion, planets appear to move from west to east over many consecutive nights as seen against the background stars. However, they occasionally (and predictably) appear to reverse direction and move east to west over consecutive nights as seen against the background stars. This backward motion is called retrograde motion.

1) Given the data in Table 1, plot the motion of the mystery planet on the graph provided in Figure 1 (record dates next to each position you plot). Then, draw a smooth line (or curve), using your data points, to illustrate the path of the planet through the sky.

Table 1 Mystery Planet Positions

Date of Observation	Azimuth (horizontal direction)	Altitude (vertical direction)
May 1	240	45
May 15	210	50
June 1	170	50
June 15	150	45
July 1	170	40
July 15	180	45
August 1	140	50
August 15	120	55

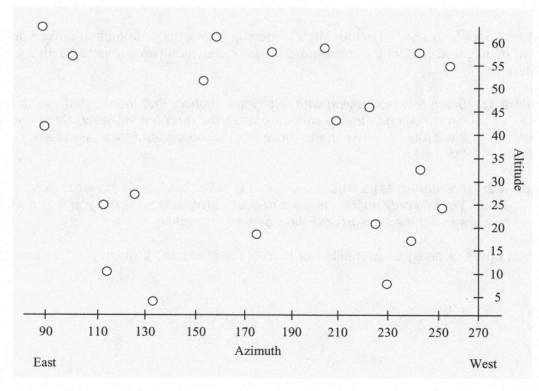

Figure 1

2) On what date was the mystery planet located farthest to the west? What was the azimuth value of the planet on this date?

3) On what date was the mystery planet located farthest to the east? What was the azimuth value of the planet on this date?

4) During which dates does the mystery planet appear to move with normal, prograde, motion, as compared to the background stars? In what direction (east-to-west or west-to-east) does the planet appear to be moving relative to the background stars during this time?

5) During which dates does this mystery planet appear to move with backward, retrograde, motion, as compared to the background stars? In what direction (east-to-west or west-to-east) does the planet appear to be moving relative to the background stars during this time?

6) If a planet were moving with retrograde motion, how would the planet appear to move across the sky in a single night? Where would it rise? Where would it set?

7) Suppose your instructor says that Mars is moving with retrograde motion tonight and will rise at midnight. Consider the following discussion between two students about motion of Mars.

Student 1: *Since Mars is moving with retrograde motion, that means that during the night it will be moving west-to-east rather than east-to-west. So at midnight it will rise in the west and move across the sky and then later set in the east.*

Student 2: *I disagree. Mars would still rise in the east and set in the west tonight. You will only notice the west-to-east retrograde motion if you watch Mars against the background stars over many nights.*

Do you agree or disagree with either or both of the students? Explain your reasoning.

The extremely high temperature of Earth's core causes material in the surrounding mantle to become hot, expand, and rise toward the surface. The mantle material then cools and sinks, resulting in a circular motion of material moving beneath Earth's surface. This circulation of mantle material causes the continental and oceanic plates to move across Earth's surface. At various locations on Earth's surface, we are able to observe plates colliding, plates separating, and plates moving horizontally with respect to each other.

The drawing below shows a cross-section of Earth's surface and its underlying mantle. At this particular location of the surface, the dense oceanic plate is being forced beneath the less dense continental crust. The dense oceanic plate experiences higher temperatures (and pressures) as it is forced deeper into the mantle. This interaction between the oceanic plate and continental plate causes molten material to move upward through the continental plate until it breaks the surface in the form of volcanoes.

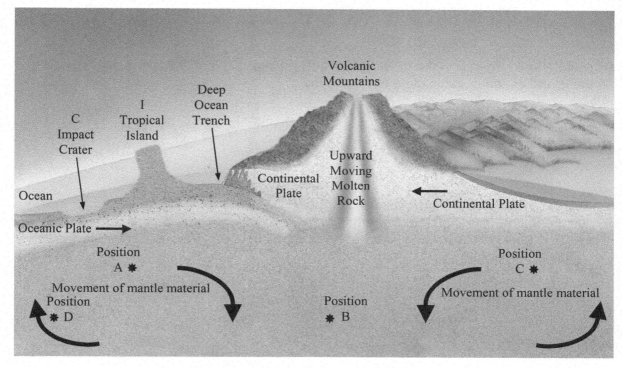

Oceanic to Continental Plate Convergence Zone

In the drawing above, Positions A–D show the position of four pieces of mantle material. Use this drawing to answer the next three questions.

1) Which direction (right or left) are the oceanic and continental plates moving?

2) Which is hotter, the piece of mantle material at Position A or the piece of mantle material at Position D? Explain your reasoning.

3) What direction are the pieces of mantle material moving (up, down, left, or right) at Positions A, B, C, and D?

4) Consider the following discussion between two students debating why the oceanic and continental plates move.

Student 1: *The plates are moving because the mantle material is constantly moving beneath Earth's plates, and this causes the plates to move.*

Student 2: *I disagree. The plates are just floating on the mantle material. The plates started moving a long time ago when Earth initially formed, and the plates' momentum keeps them moving toward each other.*

Do you agree or disagree with either or both of the students? Explain your reasoning.

5) Just beneath Point I on the drawing is a tropical island. What will eventually happen to the island as the oceanic plate moves? Why?

6) Just beneath Point C on the drawing is an ancient impact crater on the ocean floor where a giant comet collided with Earth. What will happen to the ancient impact crater as the oceanic plate moves? Why?

7) Imagine that an impact occurred on the continental plate millions and millions of years ago, leaving behind an impact crater near the right side of the base of the volcano. Why would there be little evidence of this impact crater found today?

8) Consider the image below of the rocky and crater-covered Moon. Its very old surface has remained virtually unchanged over the last few billion years. Do you think the Moon has an active, hot, and molten interior or an inactive, cold, and solid interior? Why?

9) If a new planet were discovered, what evidence would you look for to determine whether or not it has an active, hot, and molten interior? Why?

Objects give off different amounts of energy depending upon their temperature. Figure 1, below, shows the energy output of our Sun along with the percent of energy given off by the Sun in the ultraviolet (UV), visible (VIS), and infrared (IR) portions of the electromagnetic spectrum.

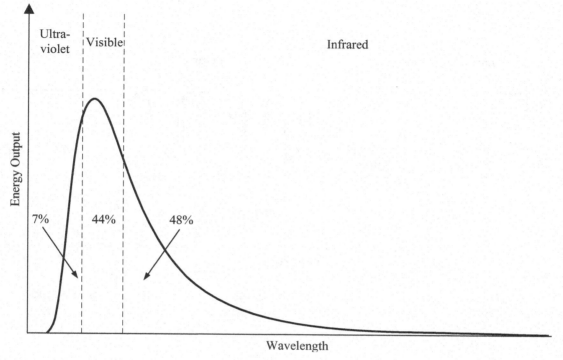

Figure 1

1) Which **TWO** forms of light account for the majority of energy coming from the Sun: ultraviolet, visible, or infrared? Which of the three forms of light is the Sun giving off the least? Provide numbers to support your answer.

ultraviolet only
7% of light under
peak is in infarred

2) Consider the following debate between two students regarding the energy given off by the Sun.

   Student 1:   *I think that the Sun gives off most of its energy at ultraviolet wavelengths because ultraviolet light is more energetic than visible light and you always hear about ultraviolet light causing sunburns.*

   Student 2:   *Even though ultraviolet light is more energetic than visible light the Sun simply gives off less ultraviolet light and gives off way more visible and infrared light. So I think these longer wavelength types of light account for most of the energy coming from the Sun.*

   Do you agree or disagree with either or both of these students? Explain your reasoning.

student 2

Earth's surface is heated by light that is absorbed at the surface. However, a photon's ability to travel through our atmosphere depends upon its wavelength. Figure 2 below shows what percentage of each type of light (UV, Visible and IR) is absorbed by Earth's atmosphere. The figure also lists the primary gas molecules responsible for absorbing the different wavelengths of light.

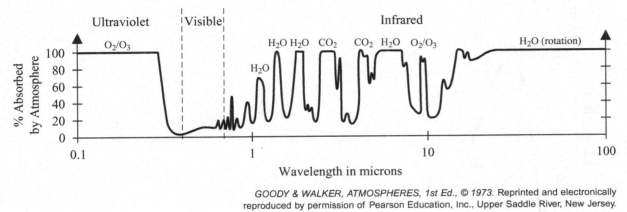

GOODY & WALKER, ATMOSPHERES, 1st Ed., © 1973. Reprinted and electronically reproduced by permission of Pearson Education, Inc., Upper Saddle River, New Jersey.

Figure 2

3) Based on the amount of visible and the infrared light being absorbed, which would you say has an easier time getting through our atmosphere? Explain your reasoning.

   lower % absorbed

4) Comparing the ultraviolet and the infrared types of light, which would you say has an easier time getting through our atmosphere? Explain your reasoning.

   more dips in % absorbed

5) Based upon Figures 1 and 2, why is ultraviolet light **NOT** an important energy source for heating the surface of Earth?   *most ultraviolet light is absorbed by our atmosphere*

6) What gas molecules are primarily responsible for the absorption of each of the following types of light in our atmosphere?

Type of Light	Molecule(s) Responsible for Absorption
Ultraviolet	O_2/O_3 ozone
Visible	
Infrared	H_2O, CO_2

Molecules that are transparent to visible light but absorb and re-emit **infrared** light are known as "greenhouse gases."

7) What are the two greenhouse gases most responsible for absorbing infrared light in Earth's atmosphere?

water and carbon dioxide

Once visible light from the Sun reaches the surface of Earth, some of the visible light is reflected back toward space and the remaining visible light is absorbed by the ground. This reflected visible light does not change the temperature of the surface, whereas absorbed visible light causes the temperature of the surface to increase. Earth's heated surface then gives off infrared light into Earth's atmosphere. As an example, on a hot day, black asphalt absorbs more visible light and gives off more infrared light than does a white crosswalk.

8) The Sun is approximately 6000 K at the surface and has an energy distribution that peaks at visible wavelengths; Earth's surface is much cooler at about 288 K. What type of light do you think Earth's surface primarily gives off: ultraviolet, visible, or (infrared) light? Explain your reasoning.

cooler which means it would emit much larger wavelengths

9) Does Earth's surface give off any form of light at night? If so, what type? If not, why not?

infarred

10) Consider the following debate between two students regarding the energy given off by Earth's surface.

Student 1: *The Sun mainly gives off visible light and so does Earth's surface because I can see it during the daytime.*

Student 2: *What you are seeing is just reflected sunlight. Earth's surface is much cooler than the Sun and mostly gives off light similar to the type that our bodies give off, infrared. I'm not sure, but I think the surface probably gives off infrared light during both the daytime and the nighttime based upon its temperature.*

Do you agree or disagree with either or both of the students? Explain your reasoning.

↳ student 2

11) Will the light given off by Earth's surface easily travel back through the atmosphere to space or will it be (absorbed) by molecules in the atmosphere? Explain your reasoning.

↳ because of greenhouse gases

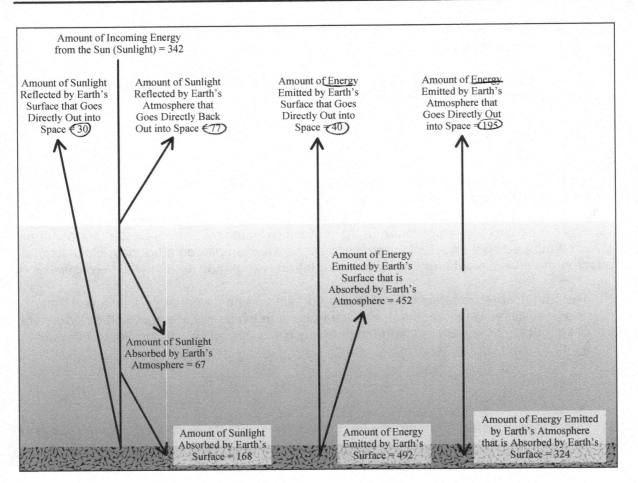

Figure 3

Figure 3 shows how light/energy flows through the Earth system for the "greenhouse effect." The numbers listed describe the amount of energy flowing through the system (units of watts per square meter). A larger number indicates that more energy is flowing through that labeled pathway.

12) How does the total amount of energy coming from the Sun compare to the total amount of energy leaving Earth to space? Provide numbers to support your answer.

→ 342

↓
195 + 40 + 77 + 30 = 342

13) What type of light contributes the greatest amount of energy to heating Earth's surface and where was this light emitted from? What type of light contributes the greatest amount of energy to heating Earth's atmosphere and where was this light emitted from?

IR   atmosphere and sun

14) Is more energy absorbed by Earth's surface in the form of light coming from the Sun or from light emitted by Earth's ~~atmosphere?~~ (atmosphere?) Explain your reasoning, and provide numbers to justify your answer.

168 vs 324

15) Due to the light absorbed by Earth's surface that was emitted by Earth's atmosphere, is Earth's temperature near the surface going to be (warmer) or cooler than it would be without this absorbed light?

16) Fill in the empty boxes in Figure 4 below with the correct type(s) of light. Use the abbreviations UV, IR, and VIS.

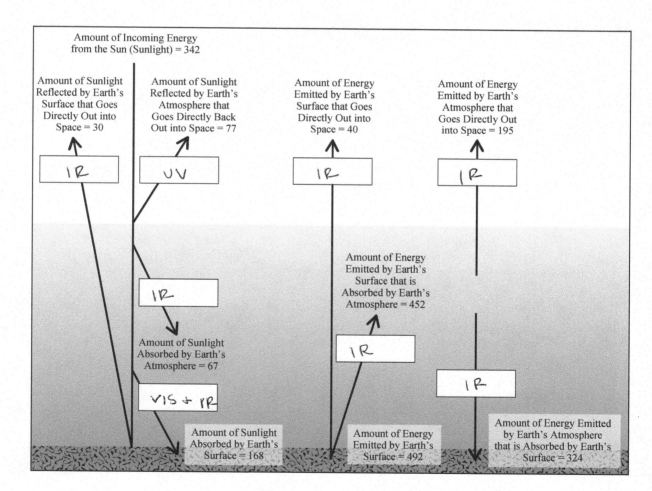

Amount of Incoming Energy from the Sun (Sunlight) = 342

Amount of Sunlight Reflected by Earth's Surface that Goes Directly Out into Space = 30
IR

Amount of Sunlight Reflected by Earth's Atmosphere that Goes Directly Back Out into Space = 77
UV

Amount of Energy Emitted by Earth's Surface that Goes Directly Out into Space = 40
IR

Amount of Energy Emitted by Earth's Atmosphere that Goes Directly Out into Space = 195
IR

IR

Amount of Sunlight Absorbed by Earth's Atmosphere = 67

Amount of Energy Emitted by Earth's Surface that is Absorbed by Earth's Atmosphere = 452
IR

VIS + IR

Amount of Sunlight Absorbed by Earth's Surface = 168

Amount of Energy Emitted by Earth's Surface = 492

IR

Amount of Energy Emitted by Earth's Atmosphere that is Absorbed by Earth's Surface = 324

Figure 4

The flow of energy shown in Figures 3 and 4 is the source of the natural "atmospheric greenhouse effect."

17) Fill in the blanks to complete the following sentences about the greenhouse effect.

VIS &
___IR___ light from the Sun passes through Earth's _atmosphere_ and is _absorbed_ by Earth's _surface_. The heated surface then gives off __IR__ light that is _absorbed_ by the _atmosphere_. The atmosphere gives off __IR__ light. Some of this light escapes out to space, but the majority is sent back to and _absorbed_ by Earth's _surface_ making the temperature warmer than it would be if there was not a _atmosphere_. Earth's surface temperature is warmer because it is heated both by _VIS & IR_ light from the _sun_ and __IR__ light sent back from the _atmosphere_.

Figure 1: A visual depiction of the planet formation process.

Figure 1 represents the different stages (a–e) in the formation of our Solar System: (a) A giant cloud of gas and dust collapses. (b) As the cloud collapses, it begins to spin, flatten, and get hotter. We refer to this spinning disk of dust and gas as a protoplanetary disk. (c/d) The majority of the mass in the disk comes together at the center and forms the Sun. The remaining rocky, icy, and gaseous material in the disk continues to interact and attract one another, forming planetesimals. (e) These planetesimals continue to collide and grow into planets over the course of tens of millions of years, eventually settling into their final locations.

1) At what location will we find the majority of material after the cloud collapses? What do we call the object that will be at this location?

   center called a star

2) Which force caused the cloud to collapse and the material to come together to form planets?

   gravity

Table 1: This table provides the condensation (becomes solid) temperature and relative abundance of three main types of materials present in the protoplanetary disk at the time of planet formation.

Material	Condensation Temp	Relative Abundance (mass %)
Hydrogen & Helium Gas	Does not condense	98
Rocks & Metals	<1600 K	0.6
Ices [hydrogen compounds (e.g., water, methane, and ammonia)]	<150 K	1.4

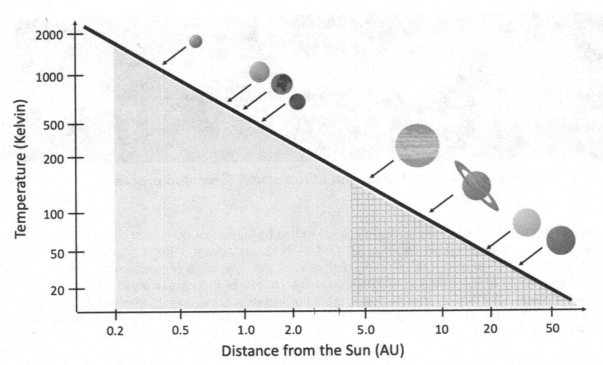

Figure 2: The graph above shows the temperature at different locations in the protoplanetary disk at the time of planet formation. The region where rock and metals condense (become solid) is shaded in light gray, and the region where hydrogen compounds (e.g., water, methane, and ammonia) condense to form ice is identified by the grid pattern. The locations of the planets are shown (the sizes of the planets on the graph are not to scale).

3) Over what range of distances did rocks and metals condense during the formation of the Solar System?

> .2 AU+0

4) Over what range of distances did hydrogen compounds condense to form ice during the formation of the Solar System?

> 4.5 AU⁺

5) Complete Table 2 below to include the planet name and the type(s) of materials (rock and/or ice) that had condensed and were present in the disk at the time of planet formation. One row of the table has been filled in for you.

Table 2: Planet distances and availability of rock, metals, and ice.

Planet Name	Distance from the Sun (AU)	What solid materials were present at the location of the planet?
mercury	0.39	rocks, metals
venus	0.72	
earth	1.00	
mars	1.52	
Jupiter	5.20	rock, metals, ice
Saturn	9.58	
Uranus	19.2	
Neptune	30.1	rock, metals, ice

Each of the three drawings below (A–C) represents a different model for the formation of the Solar System. The medium gray regions identify where the models predict only solid rocks and metals existed. The light gray regions identify where the models predict solid rock and ice both existed. The white regions identify where the models predict only ice existed. The thick black line represents the *frost line*. In the early Solar System, locations closer to the Sun than the frost line were too hot for hydrogen compounds to condense into ices. Ices could only form beyond the frost line. For each model, labels are provided next to each planet to indicate which solids existed at that location during the formation of the Solar System.

6) Based on the information provided in Figure 2 and your answers in Table 2, which of these Solar System models (A–C) most accurately shows where the solid materials were available to each planet in our Solar System while they were forming.

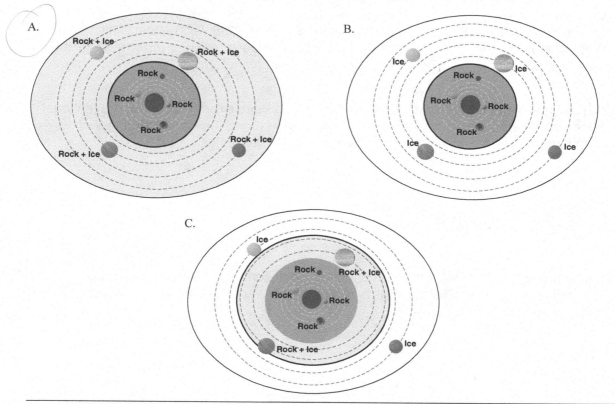

LECTURE-TUTORIALS FOR INTRODUCTORY ASTRONOMY
FOURTH EDITION

7) Three students are discussing their answer to Question 6. Recall that Mercury, Venus, Earth, and Mars are commonly referred to as the Terrestrial planets, and Jupiter, Saturn, Uranus, and Neptune are commonly referred to as the Jovian planets.

Student 1: *I think drawing "C" is correct because we know the Terrestrial planets are made of rock and Neptune and Uranus are ice giants so they will be the only planets made of just ice.*

Student 2: *I agree with you, but I think you need to include Jupiter and Saturn as having some ice too, and based on the graph the frost line should be drawn closer to the Sun than Jupiter, so I think it's drawing "B."*

Student 3: *I think you're right that the frost line should be drawn closer to the Sun, but I think drawing "A" is correct because there were rocks and metals everywhere in the early Solar System but ice only formed past the frost line so the gas giant planets should be rock and ice.*

Which students do you agree or disagree with? Explain your reasoning.

8) During the formation process, planetesimals gather up the material that was present along their orbit around the Sun. Complete the sentences below by using the words provided in the parentheses ().

The amount of solid material collected by each of the planets in the outer Solar System would have been _____ (much less / the same as / much more than) the amount of solid material collected by each of the planets in the inner Solar System. This means that the mass of the _____ (Terrestrial planets / Jovian planets) is (are) much greater than that of the _____ (Terrestrial planets / Jovian planets).

9) Which type of planets (Terrestrial or Jovian) would have exerted stronger gravitational forces when attracting the gas particles that existed along their orbits during the formation process? Explain your reasoning.

b/c they are made of gas

10) In describing types of planets, it is customary to describe those that have large atmospheres as "Gas Giants." Which of the planets in our Solar System would be considered Gas Giants?

Jovian Planets

Table 3: Properties for three planets (A, B, and C) which formed together in a Solar System around a Sun-like star.

Planet Name	Mass (Earth = 1)	Distance from star (AU)	Atmosphere (Large/Small)
A	0.643	1.774	Small
B	11.34	6.482	Large
C	12.01	0.031	Large

(handwritten notes beside table: Maybe, NO)

11) Which of these planets (A–C) are at distances from their central star that are consistent with the planet formation process of our Solar System, and which are not?

(handwritten:) B - yes   A - yes   C - NO

12) Three students are discussing a plausible explanation for why a planet might be found at a location that is not consistent with where we find planets of that type in our Solar System.

Student 1: *I think that the physics that explains where rock, metals, ice, and gas exist during the planet formation process doesn't apply when we're dealing with planets in other solar systems* *(handwritten X)*

Student 2: *I disagree. I think the locations where we'd expect to find rock, metals, ice, and gas would be pretty much the same in every Solar System. What I think happens is that the star gets way more massive after the Solar System forms, and this pulls planets closer in toward the star.* *(handwritten: shouldn't just pull big planets, X)*

Student 3: *We learned that almost all the mass of a Solar System is already in the star from essentially the beginning, and if it did get more massive it would pull all the planets closer, not just one Gas Giant. I think planets might be interacting with other objects in the Solar System, which could cause a planet to move inward from the initial position where it formed.* *(handwritten ✓)*

Which students do you agree or disagree with? Explain your reasoning.

(handwritten:) probably correct,

Part I

Figure 1: A picture of the Sun and eight planets in our Solar System (not to scale).

Table 1 below provides values for the radius (size), mass, and density for the planets in our Solar System: Mercury, Venus, Earth, Mars, Jupiter, Saturn, Uranus, and Neptune.

Table 1: Planet Properties

Planet	Radius (Earth = 1)	Mass (Earth = 1)	Density (Water = 1)
Mercury	0.383	0.055	5.43
Venus	0.949	0.815	5.25
Earth	1	1	5.52
Mars	0.532	0.107	3.93
Jupiter	11.21	317.8	1.33
Saturn	9.45	95.18	0.70
Uranus	4.01	14.54	1.28
Neptune	3.88	17.15	1.64

1) Given the data on the planet properties provided in Table 1, if you were going to sort the planets into two groups such that the planets in each group had similar properties, which planets would go into each of your two groups?

Group #1:

Group #2:

2) How would you describe the three properties that define each group (large / small size or radius, low / high mass, low / high density)?

Group #1 Properties:

Group #2 Properties:

We often categorize the planets in our Solar System as being either "Terrestrial" or "Jovian." Terrestrial planets are small, low mass, have rocky surfaces, and have higher densities (much greater than water). Jovian planets are large, massive, have gaseous outer layers, and have lower densities.

3) Which of the planets in our Solar System would you say are Terrestrial and which are Jovian?

4) Two students are discussing the composition and densities of the Jovian and Terrestrial planets.

Student 1: *I get it, since the Jovian planets are mostly made of gas, they have densities that are much lower than the Terrestrial planets that are mostly made of rock.*

Student 2: *I don't think that's right. The Jovian planets are much larger and more massive than the smaller Terrestrial planets, and therefore the Jovian planets should have much higher densities.*

Do you agree or disagree with either or both of the students? Explain your reasoning.

Part II

Table 2 below provides values for distance from the Sun, orbital period, rotational period, and number of moons for the planets in our Solar System.

Table 2: Additional Planet Properties

Planet	Distance from the Sun (AU)	Orbital Period (Years)	Rotational Period (Days)	Number of Moons
Mercury	0.387	0.241	58.6	0
Venus	0.723	0.615	243	0
Earth	1	1	1	1
Mars	1.524	1.881	1.03	2
Jupiter	5.204	11.86	0.41	79
Saturn	9.582	29.46	0.45	62
Uranus	19.19	84.01	0.72	27
Neptune	30.05	164.8	0.67	14

5) Based _only_ on the new data in Table 2, would you still sort the planets into the same two categories that you did in Part I? Why or why not?

6) Use the information from Tables 1 and 2 to help you complete the sentences below by using the words provided in the parentheses ().

The Terrestrial Planets in our Solar System: have_____ (large / small) radii, _____ large / small) mass, _____ (high / low) density, are _____ (closer to / further from) the Sun, have _____ (long / short) orbital periods, _____ (long / short) rotational periods, and have _____ (many / few) moons.

The Jovian Planets in our Solar System: have _____ (large / small) radii, _____ (large / small) mass, _____ (high / low) density, are _____ (closer to / further from) the Sun, have _____ (long / short) orbital periods, _____ (long / short) rotational periods, and have _____ (many / few) moons.

7) Which planet has a year that is slightly more than half of an Earth year, and a day that is hundreds of times longer than an Earth day? Note that this planet's day is actually longer than its year!

8) Which planet(s) take(s) more than 10 Earth years to complete one orbit around the Sun, but has (have) a day that is less than half of an Earth day?

Part III

Figure 2 and Table 3 below provide information about hypothetical "Solar System X." Solar System X has three planets, whose size and locations (relative to the Sun, Mercury, Venus, and Earth) are shown in Figure 2.

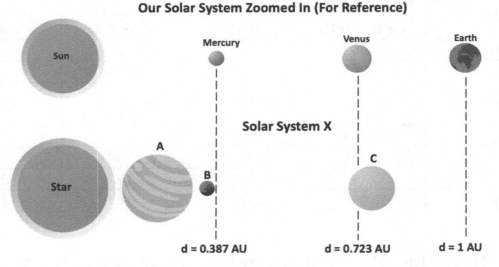

Figure 2: A visual depiction of Solar System X with respect to the Sun, Mercury, Venus, and Earth.

Table 3: Solar System X Planet Properties

Planet	Radius (Earth = 1)	Mass (Earth = 1)	Density (Water = 1)	Distance from the Star (AU)	Orbital Period (Years)
A	13.05	346.6	0.81	0.224	0.106
B	0.357	0.051	6.18	0.319	0.180
C	3.971	14.87	1.35	0.762	0.665

9) Based _only_ on their radii, masses, and densities, which planets in our Solar System are _most_ similar to the planets in Solar System X? Explain your reasoning.

10) Which of the planet(s) in Solar System X is (are) at a location(s) you would not expect based on the characteristics of the planets found in our Solar System? Explain your reasoning.

11) Two students are discussing their answer to Questions 9 and 10.

Student 1: *So Planet A is clearly Jupiter-like, but is way closer than I would have expected based on our Solar System, and Planet B seems pretty much like Mercury. I think Planet C is a Terrestrial planet because it's small and dense, roughly at the location where Venus would be in our Solar System.*

Student 2: *I agree with you about Planets A and B, but I disagree with you about Planet C. When I compare Planet C's properties to the properties of the planets in our Solar System, it seems most similar to Uranus, so I think it's more likely to be a Jovian planet even though it's close to its star.*

Do you agree or disagree with either or both of the students? Explain your reasoning.

Early in the formation of the Solar System, the four terrestrial planets were much more similar to each other than they are today. Their present-day differences are a result of geologic processes that have occurred over the last 4.5 billion years. The geologic processes that operate depend on three fundamental properties of the planets: mass, distance from the Sun, and rotation rate.

Part I: Fundamental Properties

Mass

1) Rank the four terrestrial planets (Earth, Mars, Mercury, Venus) from most massive to least massive.

    Earth> venus > mars > mercury

2) The temperature of a terrestrial planet's interior depends on its mass. Higher mass terrestrial planets have hotter internal temperatures. Rank the four terrestrial planets from hottest internal temperature to coldest internal temperature.

    " "

As a planet's internal temperature drops over time, the outer regions cool and solidify. This cold, rigid, outermost layer of a planet is known as the lithosphere.

3) If a planet is hot on the inside, would you expect it to have a thinner or thicker lithosphere than if it were cool on the inside? Explain your reasoning.

4) Do you think Earth or Mars has a thicker lithosphere? Explain your reasoning.

    cooler

5) Complete the sentences below by using the words provided in the parentheses ().

    Planets with hotter interiors will have _____ (thinner / thicker) lithospheres that are _____ (more / less) likely to crack or deform. These planets will have _____ (more / less) active volcanism and tectonics.

6) In addition to lava, volcanoes spew out large amounts of gases that, if the planet is massive enough, may be captured by the planet's gravitational pull and become part of the planet's atmosphere. Would you generally expect a more massive planet to have a thicker or a thinner atmosphere than a less massive planet? Explain your reasoning.

Distance from the Sun

7) Do you think the amount of energy received by a planet close to the Sun is greater than, less than, or the same as the amount of energy received by a planet far from the Sun? Explain your reasoning.

Below is a graph of current average surface temperatures of the terrestrial planets versus its distance from the Sun.

8) According to the graph, would you say that, in general, the surface temperature of planets appears to increase, decrease, or stay the same as their distance from the Sun increases?

9) Which do you think is more affected by distance from the Sun: surface temperature or internal temperature? Explain your reasoning.

10) Based on the graph, for which planet(s) can water currently exist as a liquid?

11) If a planet has liquid water on its surface, would you expect the planet to experience more, less, or the same amount of erosion as a planet with no liquid water? Explain your reasoning. *more sources of erosion*

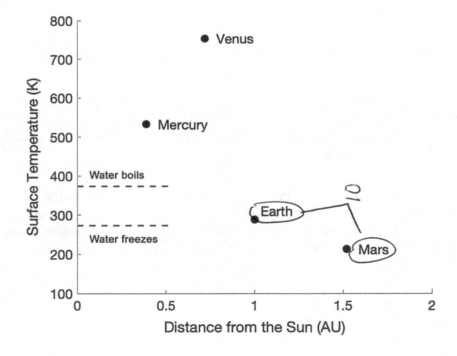

LECTURE-TUTORIALS FOR INTRODUCTORY ASTRONOMY
FOURTH EDITION

12) In our Solar System, which planet(s) should have the most erosion due to liquid water?

Earth & Mars

Rotation Rate

The rotation rates (the time for a planet to make one complete spin around its axis) and atmospheric pressure (relative to Earth) of the terrestrial planets are given in the table below.

Planet	Rotation Rate (Days)	Atmospheric Pressure
Mercury	58.6	10^{-14} times Earth
Venus	116.8	90 times Earth
Earth	1	1
Mars	1.03	0.007 times Earth

Planets that have a fast rotation rate are observed to have more weather and stronger winds than planets that have a slow rotation rate. Like having liquid on the surface, weather and wind also contribute to a planet's surface erosion. However, to have weather and winds, a planet also must have a substantial atmosphere.

13) Rank the planets based on their atmospheric pressure, from greatest to least.

Venus > Earth > Mars > Mercury

Three students are discussing how the amount of wind erosion for the four terrestrial planets will compare.

Student 1: *Earth and Mars should experience the most erosion of their surfaces due to wind because they both rotate rapidly.*

Student 2: *I agree that Earth should have erosion, but I think that Venus should also have a lot of erosion since it has such a thick atmosphere.*

Student 3: *I don't think Venus or Mars should have much wind erosion compared to Earth. Mars rotates rapidly, but its atmosphere is so thin that it wouldn't have much wind or weather. And even though Venus has a thick atmosphere, it rotates so slowly that it wouldn't have much erosion.*

agree

14) Which students do you agree or disagree with? Explain your reasoning.

Part II: Evaluating Planetary Features

15) Another geologic feature of terrestrial planets are impact craters. Do you think the number of *visible* impact craters on the surface of a planet is greater or less if volcanism, tectonics, and erosion are occurring? Explain your reasoning.

less,
covered
up

16) In the following chart, indicate which of the three fundamental planet properties influence (directly or indirectly) the three geologic processes and the number of craters that will be visible on a planet's surface. For example, mass influences the amount of volcanism present, so an "X" has been placed in that square of the table.

	Volcanism	Tectonics	Erosion	Number of Visible Impact Craters
Mass	X	X	X	X dec
Distance from Sun	⊗	⊗	X liquid	X
Rotation Rate			X	X

Because a planet's mass, distance from the Sun, and rotation rate are fundamental properties that affect planetary geology, we can predict the basic geology of newly discovered terrestrial planets once we know their fundamental properties. Suppose we discover a planet around a star similar to the Sun. We detect that the planet is less massive than the Earth, orbits about 0.7 AU from its host star, and rotates once every 12 hours.

earth also has water

48

17) Circle how you would expect this new planet to compare to Earth in the following categories:

Internal temperature:	hotter	(colder)	same
Surface temperature:	(hotter)	colder	same
Volcanism:	more	(less)	same
Tectonics:	more	(less)	same
Erosion:	more	(less)	same
Visible cratering:	(more)	less	same

Part I: Earth and Moon

Astronomers often deal with large numbers for distances, masses, and other quantities. They often use ratios to get a better sense of how big or small these quantities are. This can be useful in our daily lives as well. For example, we may not have a good sense for the length of a 40-meter-long commercial jet, but saying that the jet is approximately eight times longer than a car may be more meaningful to us. In this activity we will use ratios to try to better understand the size of objects in the Solar System, in particular the size of the Sun.

Distances such as the following can be hard to conceptualize:

Moon's diameter: 3,476 km

Earth's diameter: 12,756 km

But we can think about these sizes in terms of one another so that we can create a scale model of Earth and the Moon in our minds. If we wish to express how many times bigger Earth is than the Moon, we can divide Earth's diameter by the Moon's diameter. The result is roughly 4 (12,756/3476 ≈ 4). This means Earth is approximately four times wider than the Moon, or equivalently, you could fit about four Moons across the diameter of Earth (as shown below).

1) Which of the following pairs of objects would make a good scale model of Earth and the Moon?

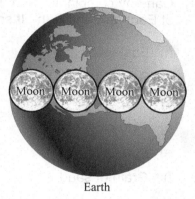

Earth

   a) A basketball and a soccer ball

   b) A basketball and a baseball (or softball)

   c) A basketball and a ping-pong ball

   d) A basketball and a pea

   e) A basketball and a grain of sand

The distance between Earth and the Moon is much larger than either the Moon or Earth—but how much larger? If we divide the distance between Earth and the Moon (384,000 km) by Earth's diameter, we get 384,400/12,756 ≈ 30. This means you could fit approximately 30 Earths in the space between Earth and the Moon.

2) Using small circles to represent Earth and the Moon, sketch a **scale model** of the Earth–Moon orbital system below. Be sure your scale model correctly shows the two scale ratios described above.

3) To make a scale model of the Earth–Moon orbital system, you not only need to pick appropriately sized objects to represent Earth and the Moon, you also need to place them the correctly scaled distance apart. Let's say you use a 1-foot (12-inch) basketball and a 3-inch orange as your Earth and Moon, respectively. About how far apart must they be placed to represent an accurate scale model of the Earth–Moon orbital system? (*Circle your answer below*.) Explain your reasoning.

    a) 1 foot

    b) 4 feet

    c) 10 feet

    d) 30 feet

    e) 300 feet

Part II: The Sun

Compared to the size of Earth, the Sun (with a diameter 1,392,000 km) is about 110 times bigger than Earth (1,392,000/12,756 ≈ 110).

4) Can any combinations of the following items be used to make an accurate scale model of Earth and the Sun? If so, which two would you choose and why? If not, why not?

    a) Basketball

    b) Soccer ball

    c) Baseball (or softball)

    d) Ping-pong ball

    e) Pea

    f) Grain of sand

Now let's compare the Sun's diameter to the size of the Moon's orbit around Earth. The diameter of the Moon's orbit around Earth is about 769,000 km across. So, the ratio of the Sun's diameter to the Moon's orbital diameter is roughly 2 (1,392,000/769,000 ≈ 2).

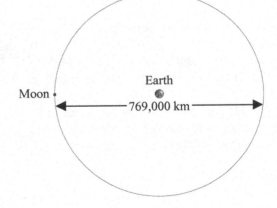

5) Does this mean that two Suns placed side-by-side would fit inside the Moon's orbit around Earth, or that two Moon orbits placed side-by-side would fit across the Sun? Draw a sketch below to illustrate your answer.

The distance from Earth to the Sun averages about 150,000,000 km. This makes the distance between the Sun and Earth about 110 times larger than the diameter of the Sun (150,000,000/1,392,000 ≈ 110).

6) If you were to use a 1-foot (12-inch) basketball to represent the Sun, how far would it have to be from Earth to be an accurate scale model?

   a) 1 foot

   b) 10 feet

   c) 30 feet

   d) 110 feet

   e) 300 feet

7) If we used a basketball to represent the Sun and a ping-pong ball to represent Earth, and separated them by the distance you answered in Question 6, would we have an accurate scale model of the Sun–Earth system? Explain your answer.

8) How many Moons would fit across the diameter of the Sun?

9) Approximately how many times could the Moon's orbital diameter fit between Earth and the Sun?

Use the H–R diagram below to answer questions throughout this activity.

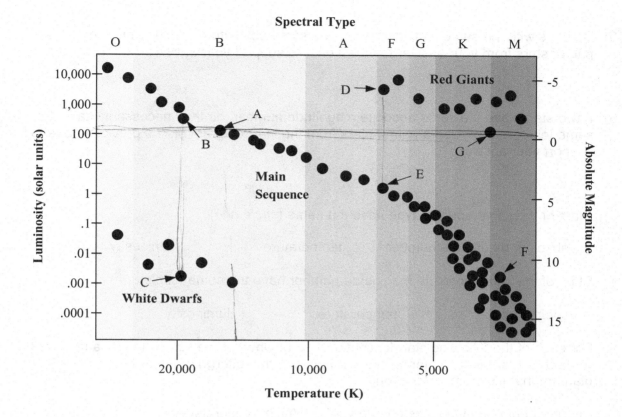

1) What are the spectral type, temperature, absolute magnitude number, and luminosity of Star A?

a) Spectral type: B

b) Temperature: 15,000 K

c) Absolute magnitude: 200 = -.5

d) Luminosity: 200

2) Which two pairs of labeled Stars (A–G) in the diagram have the same temperature?

B & C   D & E

3) Do stars of the same temperature have the same spectral type? Use a pair of stars from your answer to Question 2 to support your answer.   yes

D & E both fall under F spectral type

4) Which two pairs of labeled stars have the same luminosity?

G & A

5) Do stars with the same luminosity have the same absolute magnitude number? Use a pair of stars from your answer to Question 4 to support your answer.

yes   G & A have same luminosity & absolute mag

6) If two stars have the same absolute magnitude number, do they necessarily have the same temperature? Use a pair of stars from the H–R diagram on the previous page to support your answer.

No   G & A are at diff temp but same absolute mag

7) Stars of the same spectral type have the same (*circle one*):

   absolute magnitude number   (temperature)   luminosity

8) Stars of the same absolute magnitude number have the same (*circle one*):

   spectral type   temperature   (luminosity)

9) For each of the following star descriptions, state whether the star would be a red giant, white dwarf, or main sequence star, and provide the letter(s) of a star from the H–R diagram that fits each description.

   a) very bright (high luminosity) and very hot (high temperature)

   main seq   *A ◯*   *D*

   b) very dim and cool

   main seq

   c) very dim and very hot   *C*   *◯ B*

   white dwarf

   d) very bright and cool

   red gian

Stars begin life as a cloud of gas and dust. The birth of a star begins when a disturbance, such as the shock wave from a supernova, triggers the cloud of gas and dust to collapse inward.

1) Imagine that you are observing the region of space where a cloud of gas and dust is beginning to collapse inward to form a star (the object that initially forms in this process is called a protostar). Will the atoms in the collapsing cloud move away from one another, move closer to one another, or stay at the same locations?

2) What force causes the atoms to behave as you described they would in Question 1?

3) Would you expect the temperature at the center of the protostar to increase or decrease with time? Explain your reasoning.

The inward collapse of material causes the center of the protostar to become very hot and dense. Once the central temperature and density reach critical levels, nuclear fusion begins. During the fusion reaction, hydrogen atoms are combined together to form helium atoms. When this happens, photons of light are emitted. Once the outward pressure created by the energy given off during nuclear fusion balances the inward gravitational collapse of material, a state of *hydrostatic equilibrium* is reached, and the star no longer collapses. When this happens, the protostar becomes a main sequence star.

Consider the information shown in the table below when answering Questions 4 through 7.

Mass of the Star (in multiples of Sun masses, M_{sun})	Approximate Main Sequence Lifetime of the Star
0.5 M_{sun}	50 billion years
1.0 M_{sun}	10 billion years
2.0 M_{sun}	2 billion years
6.0 M_{sun}	110 million years
60 M_{sun}	360 thousand years

4) Which live longer, high-mass or low-mass stars?

5) Based on your answer to Question 4, do you think that the rate of nuclear fusion in a high-mass star is greater than, less than, or equal to the rate of nuclear fusion in a low-mass star?

6) Which of the following statements best describes how the lifetimes compare between Star A (a star with a mass equal to the Sun) and Star B (a star with six times the mass of the Sun)? Circle the best possible response given below. (Note: It may be helpful to examine the information given in the table on the previous page.)

a) Star A will live less than 1/6th as long as Star B.

b) Star A will live 1/6th as long as Star B.

c) Star A will have the same lifetime as Star B.

d) Star A will live six times longer than Star B.

e) Star A will live more than six times longer than Star B.

Explain your reasoning for the choice you made.

7) The Sun has a lifetime of approximately 10 billion years. If you could determine the rate of nuclear fusion for a star with twice the mass of the Sun, which of the following would best describe how its fusion rate would compare to the Sun? Circle the best possible response to complete the sentence given below. (Note: It may be helpful to examine the information given in the table on the previous page.)

A star with twice the mass of the Sun would have a rate of nuclear fusion that is _____ the rate of fusion in the Sun.

a) less than

b) a little more than

c) twice

d) more than twice

Explain your reasoning for the choice you made.

1) Imagine we measured the light emitted by a Sun-like (G-spectral type) main sequence star for several weeks. Which of the graphs below most likely shows how its graph of brightness vs. time would look (*circle A or B*)?

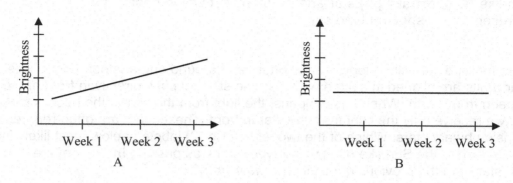

2) Imagine instead that we measure the light emitted by an A-spectral type main sequence star at the same distance as the Sun-like (G-spectral type) star from Question 1 for several weeks. Compared to the graph of the Sun-like star you chose above, which of the graphs below most likely shows how the graph of brightness vs. time would look for an A-spectral type star (*circle C or D*)?

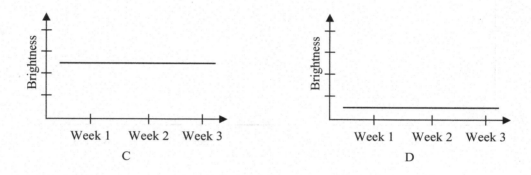

3) Imagine that these two stars are actually quite close together such that the total amount of light received from the pair can be shown in a single graph. Compared to the graphs you selected in Questions 1 and 2, which of the graphs below most likely shows how the combined graph of brightness vs. time for the two stars would look (*circle E or F*)?

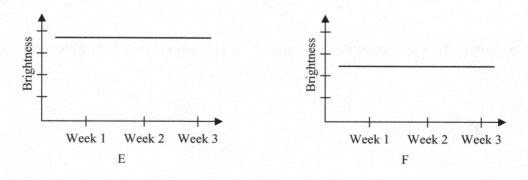

4. Imagine that the objects shown at the right represent the Sun-like and A-spectral type stars from the previous questions. Label which object would best represent the Sun-like (G-spectral type) star and which object would best represent the A-spectral type star.

5. Stars that are very close together will often orbit around one another, and, occasionally, their orbits are aligned in such a way that one star will pass directly in front of the other as seen from Earth. When this happens, the light from the star in the back is blocked, and we receive only the light from the star in front. These stars are often referred to as eclipsing binary stars. Which of the two times (1 or 2) labeled below most likely indicates the time when the Sun-like (G-spectral type) star was passing **in front** of the A-spectral type star from the previous questions (*circle 1 or 2*)?

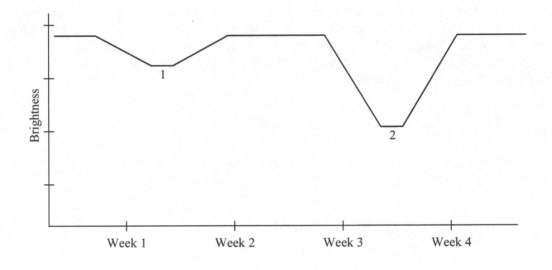

Explain your reasoning.

6) What is the physical reason the bottom of the dip is a horizontal line rather than a point?

7) Imagine that you are watching an eclipsing binary star system containing an M-spectral-type main sequence star and a B-spectral-type main sequence star as they each complete one full orbit. At Time 1, you can see that the stars are entirely separate from one another. At Time 2, you see the B star in front of the M star. At Time 3, you see the M star in front of the B star.

Use two circles of different sizes to draw the two stars at Time 1. Label which circle is the M star and which is the B star. Make two more drawings for Times 2 and 3.

8) At which of the three times would you measure the greatest amount of light coming to you? Explain your reasoning.

9) At which of the three times would you measure the least amount of light coming to you? Explain your reasoning.

10) Two students are talking about what the brightness vs. time graph would look like for eclipsing binary star system described in Question 7.

Student 1: *I think the dip in the graph is deepest when the blue star passes in front of the red star. Since the blue star is so much bigger, it will block off all of the light from the red star.*

Student 2: *I disagree, when the dim red star is in front it is blocking the more energetic light from the brighter blue star. So I think the deepest dip will happen when the M star is in front of the B star.*

Do you agree or disagree with either or both of the students? Explain your reasoning.

11) Complete the graph below to illustrate the amount of light an Earth observer would detect from an eclipsing binary star system that contains a Sun-like (G-spectral type) star and a red giant (with an orbital period of four weeks). On each dip you draw, clearly label which star is in front and which is in back.

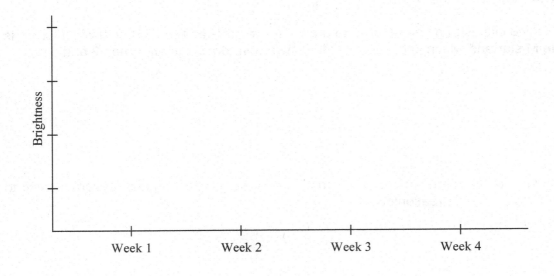

Explain your reasoning.

Part I: Extrasolar Planet Systems' Properties of Motion & Doppler Shift

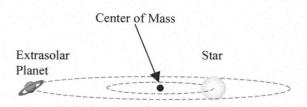

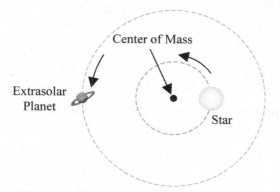

Figure 1. Extrasolar planet and star as
seen from above. (not to scale)

**Figure 2. Extrasolar planet and star as
seen edge-on or from the side. Note that
the extrasolar planet is moving toward you.**
(not to scale)

Figures 1 and 2 show the orbits of the same extrasolar planet and star from two different points of view.

1) As an extrasolar planet orbits around a star, the gravitational attraction between the two objects causes the star to make a small orbit around the system's center of mass. Which object travels in the largest orbit (*circle one*)?

the extrasolar	the star	they both have the	you can't determine
planet		same size orbit	which has the larger
			orbit

2) Which object takes a greater amount of time to complete one orbit (*circle one*)?

the extrasolar	the star	they both take the	you can't determine
planet		same amount	which takes longer
		of time	

Explain your reasoning.

3) At the instant shown in Figure 1, which direction is the extrasolar planet moving (*circle one*)?

| toward the bottom | toward the top | toward the |
| of the page | of the page | star |

4) At the instant shown in Figure 1, which direction is the star moving (*circle one*)?

toward the bottom   toward the top   toward the
of the page   of the page   extrasolar planet

5) In general, how does the direction the extrasolar planet is moving compare with the direction the star is moving?

6) If you observe the extrasolar planet system from above (as shown in Figure 1), at the instant shown, would the light from the star be blueshifted, redshifted, or not shifted? Explain your reasoning.

7) Figure 2 shows the extrasolar planet and star from the side or as seen edge-on. At the instant shown, which direction is the star moving (*circle one*)?

coming out of the page   moving into the page directly   toward the central star
directly toward you   away from you

8) If you observe the extrasolar planet system from the side, as shown in Figure 2, at the instant shown, would the light from the star be blueshifted, redshifted, or not shifted? Explain your reasoning.

9) Two students are discussing their answers to the Questions 7 and 8.

   Student 1: *Since Figure 2 states that the extrasolar planet is moving out of the page, directly toward us, then the light from the star we observe will be blueshifted.*
   Student 2: *I disagree, the light from the star will be redshifted because the star is moving in the opposite direction the planet is moving.*

Do you agree or disagree with either or both of the students? Why?

Part II: Evaluating Extrasolar Planet Systems

The amount that the light from a star in an extrasolar planet system will be Doppler shifted depends on the mass of the star M_{star}, the mass of the planet m_{planet}, and the distance d between the star and the planet. This relationship can be written as:

$$\text{Amount of Doppler shift in stars's light} \propto \frac{m_{planet}}{\sqrt{M_{star} \times d}}$$

Figure 3 below shows four different extrasolar planet systems (A–D). Use this figure to answer Questions 10 and 11.

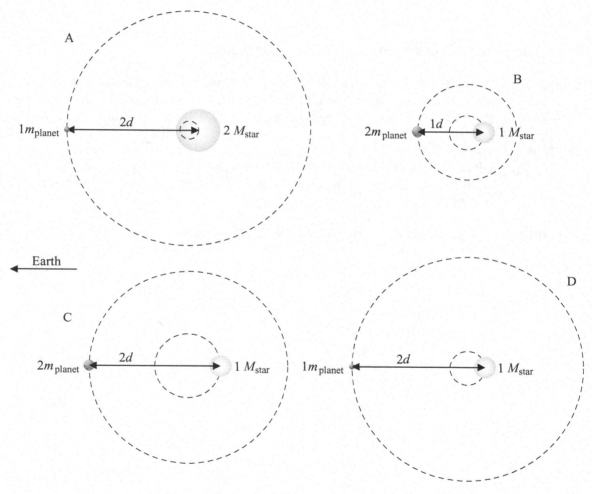

Figure 3

10) Complete the sentences below by using the words provided in the parentheses ().

The extrasolar planet that would be easiest to detect is in system ____ (A, B, C, or D) because its star gives off light that is Doppler shifted by the ____ (largest, least) amount. This occurs when a ____ (large, small) mass planet is orbiting ____ (close to, far from) a ____ (large, small) mass star, causing the star to have a ____ (fast, slow) orbital speed.

11) Two students are discussing their answers to Question 10.

Student 1: *I think the light from the star in System C would have the largest Doppler shift. This is because the star in System C has the largest orbit. And since the star's light has the largest Doppler shift that makes it and the planet easiest to detect.*

Student 2: *I agree that the easiest exoplanet to detect will correspond with the star with the largest Doppler shift. But I think the largest Doppler shift will go with System B since it has a low mass star that is close to a large mass planet.*

Do you agree or disagree with either or both of the students? Explain your reasoning.

Figure 4 below shows the graph of four radial velocity curves (E–H) for the four stars in Figure 3. Use these graphs to answer Questions 12 and 13. *Note that positive values for recessional velocity correspond with the star moving away from the observer and negative values correspond with the star moving toward the observer.*

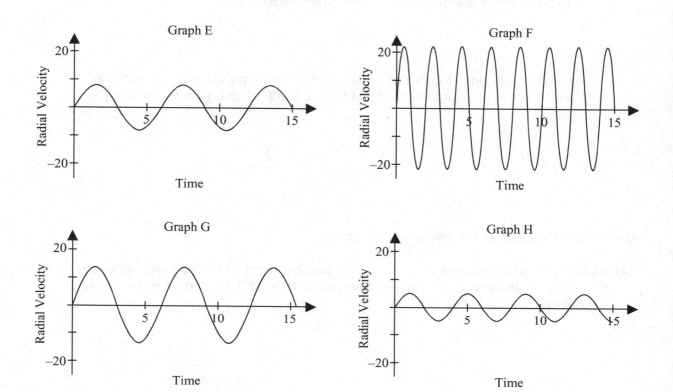

Figure 4

12) Match each graph (E–H) with the extrasolar planet systems (A–D) from Figure 3. Explain your reasoning.

Extrasolar Planet System A:

Extrasolar Planet System B:

Extrasolar Planet System C:

Extrasolar Planet System D:

13) On the graph (E, F, G, or H) that depicts the largest Doppler shift:

   a) draw a circle on the curve at each time that corresponds with the **star** moving with its fastest speed toward Earth. Explain your reasoning.

   b) draw a triangle on the curve at each time that corresponds with the **extrasolar planet** moving with its fastest speed toward Earth. Explain your reasoning.

Use Figure 5 to answer the following question.

14) Given the location marked with the dot on the star's radial velocity curve, at which location (I–L) would you expect the planet to be located at this time? Explain your reasoning.

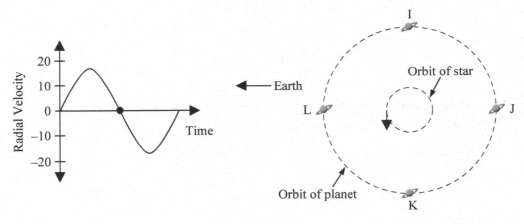

Figure 5

The Figures X, Y, and Z below show the orbits of three exoplanets around their stars.

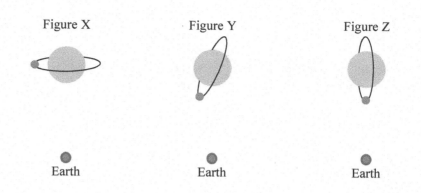

1) For each of the above Figures (X, Y, Z), could astronomers on Earth detect the presence of the exoplanet using the transit method? Explain your reasoning.

2) Imagine that you observe a star being orbited by an exoplanet. When you begin observing (Time 1), the exoplanet is in front of the star. A little later (Time 2), the exoplanet has moved so that only a fraction of its surface is in front of the star. At an even later time (Time 3), the exoplanet has moved so that no part of its surface is in front of any part of its star. In the spaces below, draw three sketches showing what the star and exoplanet would look like from your view on Earth for each of these three times described above.

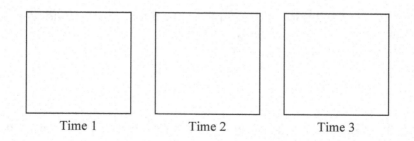

3) At which of the three times would you measure the greatest amount of light coming to you from the star? Explain your reasoning.

4) At which of the three times would you measure the least amount of light coming to you from the star? Explain your reasoning.

The graph below shows how the amount of light we detect from a star can change over time if it is orbited by an exoplanet.

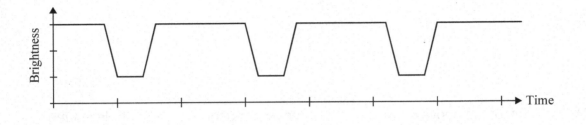

5) Using the letter "A," label the locations on the graph that correspond to the times when the exoplanet is completely in front of the star.

6) Using the letter "B," label the locations on the graph that correspond to the times when the exoplanet is not in front of the star at all.

7) Using the letter "C," label the locations on the graph that correspond to the times when the exoplanet is moving from not being in front of the star at all to being completely in front of the star. Explain your reasoning.

8) Describe what the exoplanet is doing when the light we detect from the star begins to increase from the least amount of light to the greatest amount of light.

9) Explain why the bottom of a dip in the graph is a horizontal line rather than a single point.

10) In the below figure, four different exoplanet systems are shown on the left, and four different graphs of brightness vs. time are shown on the right. Match each exoplanet system with the graph that best represents the brightness we would observe for the exoplanet system. All the stars are identical and each exoplanet crosses directly between its parent star and Earth.

Recall that the size of an exoplanet affects how much light it blocks, and that the distance between an exoplanet and its parent star affects how long the planet takes to complete an orbit around its parent star.

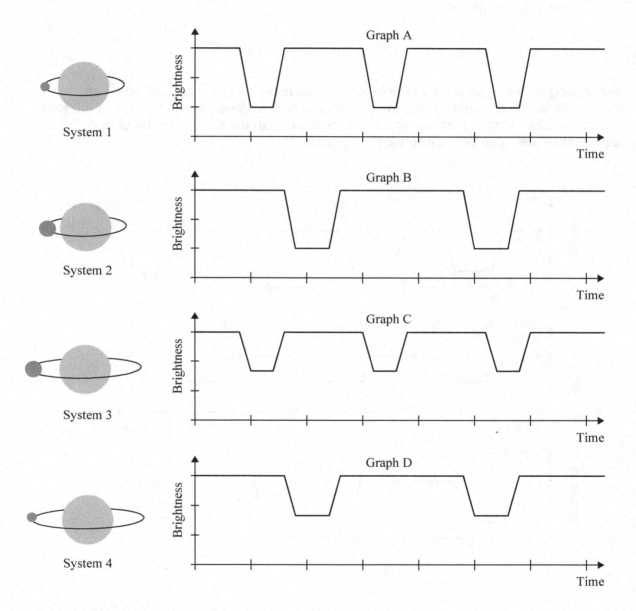

Explain your reasoning for the matches you chose.

11) Imagine you are an astronomer outside our Solar System. How long would you have to observe the Sun in order to detect four dips in the Sun's brightness due to Earth? Explain your reasoning.

12) If you can only observe a star for a limited amount of time (*e.g.*, 6 months), are you more likely to find planets that orbit close to their star or far away from their star? Explain your reasoning.

When judging a brightness vs. time graph to determine if it could be caused by an exoplanet, we must consider that the planet causes the same size and shape of dip each time it transits the star, and the dips occur regularly with the same amount of time between dips. Below are three brightness vs. time graphs.

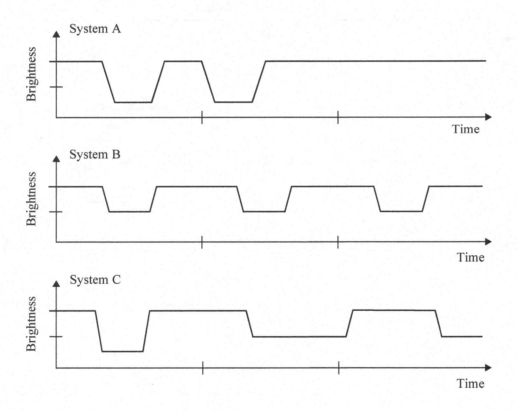

13) How many of these graphs match what you should see if each star is orbited by only one exoplanet? Explain your reasoning.

The graph below shows the observed brightness of a star over time.

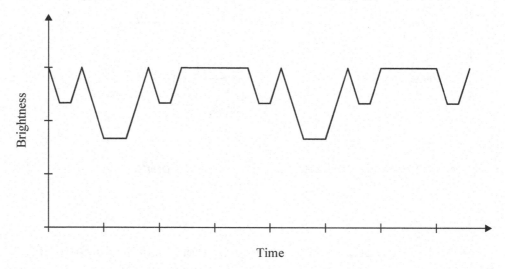

Time

14) How many exoplanets likely orbit this star? Explain your reasoning.

15) Based on the information in the graph above, complete the blanks in the sentence below by circling the correct words or phrases.

The _____ (larger / smaller) exoplanet is _____ (closer to / further from) its parent star and the _____ (larger / smaller) exoplanet is _____ (closer to / further from) its parent star.

16) Imagine an alien astronomer is observing our Sun. Their telescope is sensitive enough to detect the transits of the two largest planets in our Solar System, Jupiter and Saturn. Sketch the brightness vs. time graph the alien astronomer would produce if they observe our Solar System continuously for 27 years, starting at the instant Saturn is just beginning to move in front of the Sun. Note: Jupiter takes 12 years to orbit the Sun and Saturn takes 29 years. Jupiter is approximately 10% larger than Saturn.

The graph below shows how much visible light we receive from a star over a period of time. Use this graph to answer the following three questions

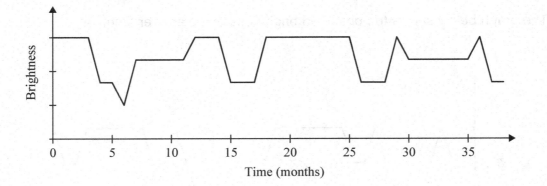

17) How many exoplanets orbit this star? Explain your reasoning.

18) How do the sizes and orbital periods of the exoplanets compare to each other? Explain your reasoning.

19) Draw a sketch of the star and exoplanets.

Main sequence stars that can no longer support nuclear fusion of hydrogen in their cores will become red giant stars. Although most main sequence stars become red giants, their specific evolutionary paths after this red giant phase vary greatly, depending on mass.

Low mass main sequence stars, those with a mass less than eight times the mass of the Sun ($<8m_s$), eventually eject their outer layers to produce a planetary nebula. The stellar core remaining in the middle of this planetary nebula is called a white dwarf.

In contrast, high mass main sequence stars, those with a mass more than eight times the mass of the Sun ($>8m_s$), eventually explode as a Type II supernova. Depending on the original mass of the star, the Type II supernova will leave behind either a neutron star or, if the original star was extremely massive, a black hole.

1) Use the information above and the word list below to fill in the ovals in the diagram on the next page. Be sure to look at the arrows and words between the ovals to make sure these links between ovals make sense. Check your work with another group.

> **Word list:**
> neutron star
> black hole
> planetary nebula
> white dwarf
> Type II supernova

The diagram does not give us all the information known about the death of stars. Since it is incomplete, we can always add to this diagram as we learn more information.

2) In Parts a and b below, you are given some additional information about the end states of stars. Your task is to change or add to the diagram to incorporate this additional information.

a) If a white dwarf has a nearby binary companion star, it can gravitationally attract material from its companion in a process known as accretion. When the white dwarf accretes enough material from the companion, the white dwarf will either (1) blow off the outer layers of accreted material in a controlled fusion reaction known as a nova, leaving behind the white dwarf unchanged and able to restart the process, or (2) experience a violent, uncontrolled fusion reaction that causes the white dwarf and accreted material to violently explode as a Type Ia supernova, destroying the white dwarf and leaving nothing behind.

b) Completely by itself in space, a black hole can be nearly impossible to detect. However, if a black hole has a nearby binary companion star, the strong gravitational pull of the black hole can attract material from its companion in a process known as accretion. This material then spirals around the black hole and increases in temperature. This process causes the rapidly moving material to emit large amounts of X-ray radiation, which we can detect with X-ray telescopes. Thus, one way to look for black holes is to look for strong X-ray sources.

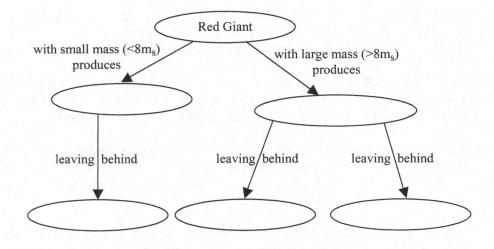

This tutorial will give you a better understanding of the size of the Milky Way Galaxy by investigating the distances and sizes of objects within the Milky Way Galaxy and outside the Milky Way Galaxy elsewhere in the universe. Below is a picture of a spiral galaxy similar to the Milky Way. Because we are located within the Milky Way, we are unable to take a picture of our entire galaxy from the outside. Let's assume that this picture represents our Milky Way Galaxy and has the dimensions labeled below. **Note that in this picture, 1 centimeter (cm) represents 10,000 light-years (ly); equivalently, you can use 1 millimeter (mm) to represent 1,000 light-years (ly).**

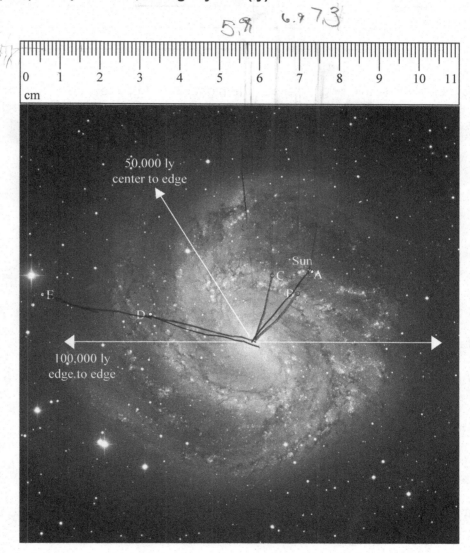

1) The Sun's position in the Milky Way is shown in the picture above. What is the approximate distance from the Sun to the center of the Milky Way? Recall that 1 cm represents 10,000 ly.

14,000 ly

2) Estimate the distances from the center of the Milky Way to the locations A-E, and record your answers (in light-years) in the table below.

Galaxy Location	Estimated Location (ly)
a)	23,000
b)	16,000
c)	18,000
d)	28,000
e)	60,000

3) The table below lists five bright stars in the night sky. Write the letter of the dot (A–E) from the picture on the previous page that best represents the location of each star. **You can use letters more than once**. Recall that 1 mm represents 1,000 ly.

Star	Distance from Sun (in light-years)	Letter
Sirius	9	a
Vega	26	a
Spica	260	a
Rigel	810	a
Deneb	1,400	a

4) Two students are discussing their answers to Question 3.

Student 1: *Since Sirius is closest, it is at A. Vega is the next closest, so it is at B. Spica is at C, Rigel at D, and Deneb, the most distant, is at E, the farthest point from the Sun.*

Student 2: *But Deneb, the farthest star, is 1,400 light-years away. 1 mm is 1,000 light-years, so Deneb should only be a little more than a millimeter from the Sun on the picture. I think all five stars are close enough to the Sun that they all correspond to letter A.*

Do you agree or disagree with either of both of the students? Explain your reasoning.

I want to agree with student 1, but the distance indicates that all of the stars should be close to the sun.

5) We normally consider Deneb to be a bright but distant star at 1,400 ly away from the Sun. Compared to the size of our Milky Way Galaxy, is Deneb truly distant? Explain your reasoning.

no, because in the grand scheme of the Milky way, it takes 10's of thousands of ly to appear "far"

LECTURE-TUTORIALS FOR INTRODUCTORY ASTRONOMY
                                                    FOURTH EDITION

6) Are the stars from Question 3 inside or outside the Milky Way Galaxy? Explain your reasoning.

I think they are all in the Milky Way Galaxy because they all center around the center of the Milky Way.

7) The table below lists three Messier objects and their distances from the Sun. Write the letter of the dot (A–E) from the picture on the previous page that best represents the location of each object. You can use letters more than once and there is more than one right answer.

Messier Object	Distance from Sun (in light-years)	Letter
M45 Open Cluster (Pleiades)	380	a
M1 (Crab Nebula)	6,300	b
M71 Globular Cluster	12,700	c

8) Are these Messier objects part of the Milky Way Galaxy? Explain your reasoning.

Yes, because they are all close to the sun which is in the Milky Way, so they must be in it too.

9) The Crab Nebula has a width of about 11 light-years. If you wanted to accurately draw the Crab Nebula on your diagram, would you use a small blob or a tiny dot at the location you indicated in Question 7? Explain your reasoning. Note: The dots marking the locations on the picture are about 1 mm across.

I would use a tiny dot because the scale factor of our image is 1mm = 1,000 ly so a blob would be too big.

10) The Sun is much smaller than a nebula. We used a dot to represent the Sun's location in the picture. Is this dot too small, too large, or just the right size to represent the size of the Sun in the picture? Explain your reasoning.

It is too big because it would need to be scaled-down to be proportional to other objects in the galaxy.

11) The Milky Way Galaxy is one of the largest galaxies in a group of nearby galaxies called the Local Group. The following table lists the distances to the centers of three Local Group galaxies. Draw a dot on your picture (if possible) to represent the center of each galaxy. Don't worry about the direction (left/right/up/down) for each galaxy; just place a dot an appropriate distance from the Sun.

Galaxy	Distance from Sun (in light-years)
Sagittarius Dwarf Elliptical Galaxy (SagDEG)—closest galaxy to Milky Way	80,000
Large Magellanic Cloud (LMC)	160,000
Andromeda Galaxy (M31)	2,500,000

Do any of these galaxies fit on the page? Which one(s)?

only SagDEG

12) Are the objects listed in Question 11 inside or outside the Milky Way? Explain your reasoning.

They are outside the MW because they are so far that I cannot even draw them on the page.

13) SagDEG is approximately 11,000 ly across. Is this galaxy better represented on your diagram by a small blob or a tiny dot? Explain your reasoning, and make an appropriate sketch to represent the galaxy.

a small blob 1.1cm across would be best because it would be to-scale of our drawing.

14) Within the Local Group, the two largest galaxies are the Milky Way and Andromeda Galaxies. From Question 11, we saw that the Andromeda Galaxy was about 2,500,000 ly from us. On the picture, this spot would be 250 cm (about two-and-a-half meters or 8 feet) away from the dot representing the Sun.

The nearest group of galaxies to us (not counting our own Local Group) is the Virgo Cluster, about 60,000,000 ly away. How many centimeters away would this cluster be on our picture? How many meters away would this be?

6,000 cm

60 m

When stars are viewed through a telescope, they typically appear as bright points of light without any apparent size or structure. However, there are some objects in the sky that, when viewed through a telescope, look "fuzzy" and cloudlike. Some of these objects, like those shown in the *Hubble Space Telescope* image to the right, are actually galaxies (containing billions of stars) that are much farther from us than the individual stars we see in the night sky.

Part I: Applying Hubble's Classification Scheme

1) Using the images of galaxies provided on the inside back cover of your *Lecture-Tutorial* book, sort these galaxies (using Hubble's categories) as being either an elliptical or a spiral galaxy. Use the table below to record your results. Try to find patterns in terms of shape, size, color, or any other distinct features that help in sorting the galaxies.

Hubble's Categories	Galaxy Numbers	Defining Characteristics (Describe the characteristics that you used to distinguish one class of galaxy from the other)
Elliptical	1358	– bright yellowish orange – no bar
Spiral	2407	– flat disk w/ bulge in the middle

Part II: Understanding the Types of Galaxies

In Part I you classified the galaxies into different categories according to their appearance, or *morphology*. We will now investigate what a galaxy's morphology can tell us about its physical characteristics. These physical characteristics include: (a) the ages of the stars in the galaxy; (b) the presence or absence of dust in the galaxy; and (c) the presence or absence of gas and star formation. The objective of this activity is for you to learn how these characteristics are related to galaxy classification and morphology.

The Ages of Stars:

2) Which of the galaxies appear to be mostly red? (Note: The word "red" is used to also include the colors orange and yellow.) Record the number and classification (elliptical or spiral) of each galaxy. Why do you think these galaxies appear red?

    1358 - no longer forming new stars

3) Which of the galaxies appear to be mostly blue? Record the number and classification (elliptical or spiral) of each galaxy. Why do you think these galaxies appear blue?

    2467 - still forming new stars

4) Which types of galaxies appear to have many young stars: elliptical, spiral, or both? Explain your reasoning.

    blue → forming new stars still

5) Do the galaxies that you identified in Question 4 also contain old stars? Explain your reasoning.

    yes - center buldge

Dust in Galaxies:

Besides stars, galaxies sometimes also contain dust. This dust produces dark bands across, or patches in, the galaxy.

6) Which of the galaxies show evidence of dust? Record the number and classification (elliptical or spiral) of each galaxy.

    2467

Gas and Star Formation in Galaxies:

In addition to stars and dust, galaxies may also contain gas.

7) Would you say that a galaxy that is experiencing active star formation contains little or (abundant) gas? Explain your reasoning.

   ↳ have to be able to make new stars

8) Which type of galaxy (elliptical or (spiral)) would have abundant gas available? Explain your reasoning.

   ↳ new stars

9) Which type of galaxy (elliptical, (spiral), both, or neither) is likely to contain both O-spectral type stars as well as M-spectral type stars? Explain your reasoning.

   ↳ O produces blue light
   and elliptical galaxies
   have no blue light seen

10) Which type of galaxy ((elliptical), spiral, both, or neither) is likely to contain many M-spectral type stars but very few (if any) O-spectral type stars? Explain your reasoning.

   No blue light
   - appears yellow/red -M type

11) Which type of galaxy (elliptical, spiral, both, or (neither)) is likely to contain only O-spectral type stars? Explain your reasoning. ↓

   all
   red   some red + blue   all
                                          blue

12) Consider the discussion among three students about a galaxy that appears red. — *elliptical*

Student 1: *agree* *Because there is mainly red light in this galaxy and no blue light, I think that only small, red stars formed in this galaxy and not any big, blue ones.*

Student 2: *hubble thought* *I disagree. It's just that blue stars don't last very long. I think the blue stars that may have been there in the past have already evolved into red giants, so the galaxy looks red due to the light from all the red giants.* *live short*

Student 3: *Wait a minute. I think you are both wrong. I thought that both blue stars and red giants live short lives, so they should both be gone. I think that all the blue stars that formed early on have evolved into the red stars that are there now. So the galaxy appears red because it's full of a lot of old, red stars that used to be the blue stars.*

Do you agree or disagree with any or all of the students? Explain your reasoning.

↓
all of them

13) Hubble imagined the tuning fork diagram (shown at right) as representing an evolutionary sequence for galaxies, with galaxies starting off as elliptical and developing more structure over time. Do you think Hubble's proposed evolutionary sequence is correct? Why or why not?

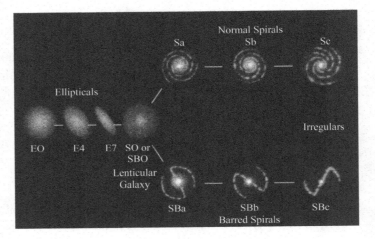

Part I: Motions of Planets

An object's orbit depends on the "mass inside" its orbit (also known as the *interior mass*). For a planet in our solar system, you can find the interior mass by adding the Sun's mass to the mass of each object between the Sun and the planet's orbit. For example, the interior mass to Earth's orbit would be the Sun's mass plus the mass of Mercury plus the mass of Venus.

Here is a table that lists each planet, the mass inside each planet's orbit, and the speed at which the planets orbit the Sun.

Planet	Interior Mass (solar masses)	Orbital Speed (km/s)
Mercury	1.00	47.9
Venus	1.00000017	35.0
Earth	1.0000026	29.8
Mars	1.0000056	24.1
Jupiter	1.0000059	13.1
Saturn	1.00096	9.66
Uranus	1.0012	6.81
Neptune	1.0013	5.43

1) Where is the vast majority of mass in the solar system located? What object or objects account for most of this mass?

2) Two students are discussing their answers to Question 1:

Student 1: *I think the majority of the mass in the Solar System must include both the Sun and the planets. As you get farther away from the Sun, the interior mass gets bigger and bigger because you include more planets.*

Student 2: *The majority of the mass in the Solar System is from just the Sun by itself. Sure the mass gets a little bigger as you include more planets, but the additional mass from planets is really small, so as you move farther out the interior mass is essentially just staying the same.*

Do you agree or disagree with either or both of the students? Explain your reasoning.

3) How do the orbital speeds of planets farther from the Sun compare to the orbital speeds of planets closer to the Sun?

get slow farther away

A planet's orbital speed depends on the gravitational force it feels. The strength of the gravitational force depends on the amount of mass that is inside of the planet's orbit as well as how far away the planet is from this interior mass.

4) How does the gravitational force on a planet far from the Sun compare to the gravitational force on a planet close to the Sun? Explain your reasoning.

↳ larger

5) Complete the blanks in the sentences of the following paragraph by either writing in the necessary information or circling the correct response in the parentheses (). It may be helpful to base your responses on the information provided in the table above and your answers to the previous questions.

There are ____ planets inside Neptune's orbit and ____ planets inside Mercury's orbit. However, the interior mass for Neptune is ____ (much greater than/approximately the same as/much less than) the interior mass of Mercury. Neptune is ____ (much closer to/much farther from/about the same distance from) the Sun as/than Mercury. Therefore the gravitational force exerted on Neptune is ____ (stronger/weaker/about the same strength) as/than the force exerted on Mercury. As a result, Neptune has an orbital speed that is ____ (much slower/much faster/about the same speed) as/than the orbital speed of Mercury.

Imagine you were able to add a very, very large amount of mass distributed evenly, like a large ring of matter, between the orbits of Jupiter and Saturn.

6) Which planet(s) will experience an increase in gravitational force and an increase in orbital speed from this added mass? Explain your reasoning.

Part II: Motions of Stars

One way to estimate the amount of mass in a spiral galaxy is by looking at how much light the galaxy emits. Where there is more light, there must be more stars and hence more mass. When astronomers measure the amount of light emitted by different regions of a galaxy, they often find that more light is emitted from the central region of the galaxy and less light is emitted from the outer regions.

7) Based on the information provided above, where do you expect most of the mass of a galaxy to be located?

Center

At right is picture of a spiral galaxy similar to the Milky Way. The orbits of three stars are labeled. Star A is a star on the edge of the Milky Way's bulge. The Sun's orbit is shown at approximately the correct position. Star B is a star located farther out in the disk than the Sun.

8) Based on your answer to Question 7 and the location of each star from the center of the galaxy, rank how you think the orbital speeds of Star A, Star B, and the Sun would compare from fastest to slowest. Explain your reasoning.

same

A graph of the orbital speed of stars vs. their distance from the galaxy's center is called a *rotation curve*. Here are two possible rotation curves.

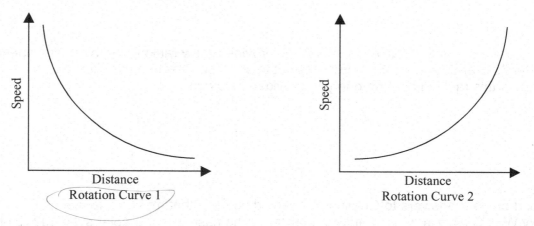

9) Which of the above rotation curves best represents the relationship you described in Question 8? Explain your reasoning.

Astronomers were surprised when they saw the real rotation curve for the Milky Way Galaxy (MWG). The rotation curve at the right is more like the MWG's real rotation curve.

10) Based on their orbital distance from the center of the galaxy, make three dots on the above rotation curve to represent Star A, Star B, and the Sun. Be sure to label which mark belongs to each star. Note that information about the distances of Stars A, B and the Sun are provided in the text before Question 8.

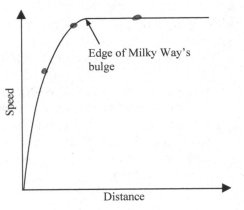

11) Describe how the stars' orbital speeds shown in the real rotation curve for the MWG are different from the orbital speeds shown in the rotation curve you chose in Question 9.

12) Using the real rotation curve for the MWG, provide a new ranking for the orbital speeds of Star A, Star B, and the Sun, from fastest to slowest. Describe any differences between this ranking and the one you provided in Question 8.

13) Based on your answers to Question 12, would you say that most of the mass of the Milky Way Galaxy is located at its center (as is the case with our solar system)? Explain your reasoning.

14) Based on the MWG's real rotation curve and your answers to Questions 11–13, is the gravitational force felt by Star A, Star B and the Sun greater than, less than, or about the same as what you expected from Questions 8 and 9? Explain your reasoning.

15) Two students are debating their answers to the previous questions:

Student 1: Stars far from the center of the Milky Way are all moving at about the same speed. If most of the Milky Way's mass is located in its center, then stars far away from the center would orbit slower than stars closer to the center. Since this is not what we see, this must mean there is more mass throughout the outer regions of the galaxy than we can see. This also means that the Milky Way's stars feel a greater gravitational force than we originally expected.

Student 2: I disagree. There are fewer stars in the outskirts of the Milky Way than in the center, so there's less mass out there than at the center. Most of the Milky Way's mass must be at its center. So, since the stars are all going about the same speed, where the mass is located must not affect their speed. The gravitational force these stars feel probably gets weaker just like we would expect.

Do you agree or disagree with either or both of the students? Explain your reasoning.

16) Is there more or less mass in the Milky Way's disk and halo than we can see? Explain your reasoning.

LECTURE-TUTORIALS FOR INTRODUCTORY ASTRONOMY
FOURTH EDITION

Imagine that you have received six pictures of six different children who live near six of the closest stars to the Sun. Each picture shows a child on his or her 12th birthday. The pictures were each broadcast directly to you (using a satellite) on the day of the child's birthday. Note the abbreviation "ly" is used below to represent a light-year.

- Benjamin lives on a planet orbiting Ross 154, which is 9.5 ly from the Sun.
- Natalie lives on a planet orbiting Barnard's Star, which is 6.0 ly from the Sun.
- Dale lives on a planet orbiting Sirius, which is 8.6 ly from the Sun.
- Sydney lives on a planet orbiting Alpha Centauri, which is 4.3 ly from the Sun.
- Joyce lives on a planet orbiting Epsilon Eridani, which is 10.8 ly from the Sun.
- Crystal lives on a planet orbiting Procyon, which is 11.4 ly from the Sun.

1) Describe in detail what a light-year is. Is it an interval of time, a measure of length, or an indication of speed? It can only be one of these quantities.

   a ly is a measure of length that describes the distance between the Earth & the Sun.

2) Which child lives closest to the Sun? How far away does he or she live?

   Sydney b/c she lives 4.3ly away.

3) What was the greatest amount of time that it took for any one of the pictures to travel from the child to you?

   11.4 years (crystal)

4) If each child was 12 years old when he or she sent his or her picture to you, how old was each of the children when you received their picture?

   Benjamin *13.5* Natalie *18* Dale *20.6*
   Sydney *16.3* Joyce *22.8* Crystal *23.4*

5) Complete the blanks in the sentences of the following paragraph by circling the correct response in the parentheses ().

   The light from the child that is farthest from Earth will take the ____ (greatest/least) amount of time to get to us. The child will be getting older this entire time, and therefore will be the ____ (oldest/youngest) of all the children at the time when we receive their picture.

6) Imagine that the six pictures of the children all arrived at exactly the same time. For this to happen, could the children have all sent their pictures at the same time? If not, which child sent his or her picture first and which child sent his or her picture last?

   NO, they would have needed to space their outgoing message proportional to their relative distance

7) The telescope image at the right was taken of the Andromeda Galaxy, which is located about 2.5 million ly away from us. Is this an image showing how the Andromeda Galaxy looks right now, how it looked in the past, or how it will look in the future? Explain your reasoning.

Photo Credit: Stocktrek Images, Inc./ Alamy Stock Photo

Past b/c it takes 2.5 million years for the light of the andromeda galaxy to reach us.

8) Imagine that you are observing the light from a distant star that was located in a galaxy 100 million ly away from you. By analysis of the starlight received, you are able to tell that the image we see is of a 10-million-year-old star. You are also able to predict that the star will have a total lifetime of 50 million years, at which point it will end in a catastrophic supernova.

a) How old does the star appear to be to us here on Earth?

10 million yrs old

b) How long will it be before we receive the light from the supernova event?

40 million years

c) Has the supernova already occurred? If so, when did it occur?

yes, it occured 60 million years ago?

9) Imagine that you take images of two main sequence stars that have the same mass. From your observations, both stars *appear* to be the same age. Consider the following possible interpretations that could be made from your observations.

a) Both stars are the same age and the same distance from you.
b) Both stars are the same age but at different distances from you.
c) The stars are actually different ages but at the same distance from you.
d) The star that is closer to you is actually the older of the two stars.
e) The star that is farther from you is actually the older of the two stars.

How many of the five choices (a–e) are possible? Which ones? Explain your reasoning.

a - same age & same amount of time to recieve light

d - shorter distance = shorter amount of time to receive light

The two drawings below represent the same group of galaxies at two different points in time during the history of the universe.

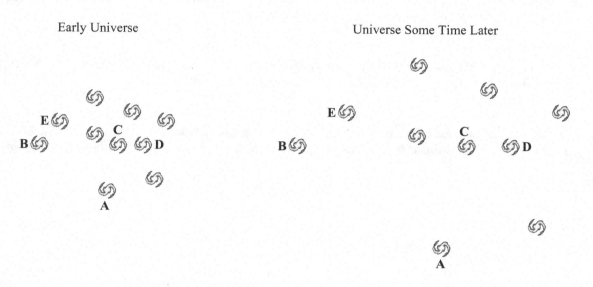

Early Universe

Universe Some Time Later

1) Examine the distance between the galaxies labeled A–E in the Early Universe. Are all the galaxies the same distance from each other?

NO

2) Describe how the universe changed in going from the Early Universe to the Universe Some Time Later.

moved away from each other

3) Do the galaxies appear to get bigger?

NO

4) Based on your answer to Question 3, do you think the stars within a galaxy move away from one another due to the expansion of the universe? Explain your reasoning.

yes

5) Compare the amount that the distance between the D and C galaxies changed in comparison to the amount that the distance between the D and E galaxies changed. Which galaxy, C or E, appears to have moved farther from D?

E

6) If you were in the D galaxy, how would the A, B, C, and E galaxies appear to move relative to your location?

down | left   left + up
left

7) If you were in the D galaxy, would the A, B, C, and E galaxies all appear to move the same distance in the time interval from the Early Universe to the Universe Some Time Later?

NO

8) Imagine that you are still in Galaxy D. Rank the A, B, C, and E galaxies in terms of their relative speeds away from you, from fastest to slowest.

C < A < E < B

9) Now imagine that you are in the E galaxy. Rank the A, B, C, and D galaxies in terms of their relative speeds away from you, from fastest to slowest.

about
D = A > C > B

10) Is there a relationship between an object's distance away from you in the universe and the speed it would appear to be moving away from you? If so, describe this relationship.

moving faster away from you the farther away it is in the beginning

11) Would your answer to Question 10 be true in general for all locations in the universe?

yes

12) Consider the following discussion between two students regarding the possible location of the center of the universe.

Student 1: *Since all the galaxies we observe are moving away from us, we must be at the center of the universe.*

Student 2: *If you look at the drawing on the first page, it's pretty clear that all the galaxies move away from each other, so I think each galaxy must be at the center of the universe.*

Do you agree or disagree with either or both of the students? Explain your reasoning.

both
Why? No center to universe

Part I: Understanding Hubble-Lemaître Law and Hubble Plots

The Hubble-Lemaitre law states that the farther away a galaxy is, the faster the galaxy will be moving away from the observer. We can depict Hubble-Lemaître law with the graph shown at right. This graph plots the speed at which a galaxy appears to move away from us versus its distance from us. This type of graph is called a *Hubble plot*. Each dot on the plot represents a different galaxy.

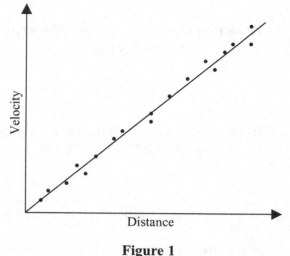

Figure 1

1) Complete the sentences below by using the words provided in the parentheses ().

   Galaxies that are very far away from us appear to move _____ (away/toward) us at _____ (slower/faster) speeds than galaxies that are closer to us."

2) Imagine the Hubble plot shown in Figure 1 represents observations of the universe that suggest its doubling in size over a certain amount of time. Which of the Hubble plots shown in Figures 2 and 3 would represent observations of our universe suggesting it is tripling in size over the same amount of time? Explain your reasoning.

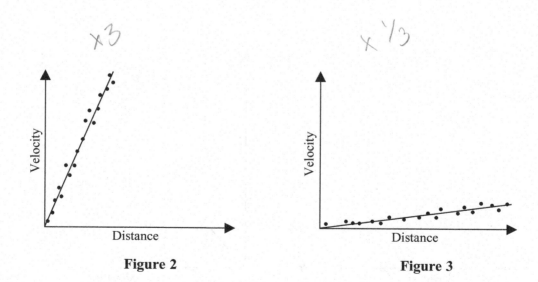

Figure 2

Figure 3

The *expansion rate* of the universe determines how fast the universe increases in size with time. For example, if our universe were tripling in size, it would have a faster expansion rate than if it were doubling in size over the same amount of time. In a Hubble plot, the *expansion rate* is indicated by the slope of the graph. A steep slope indicates a fast expansion rate, while a flat slope indicates a slow expansion rate.

3) Would you say the expansion rate for the universe represented in Figure 1 is increasing, decreasing, or constant with time? Explain your reasoning.

increasing

4) Rank (from fastest to slowest) the expansion rates represented in Figures 1, 2, and 3. Explain your reasoning.

2 > 1 > 3

5) If the expansion rate of our universe had been faster, would the universe have reached its current size earlier in its history or later? Explain your reasoning.

earlier

6) Complete the sentence below using the words provided in parentheses ().

   If you create a Hubble plots from two different sets of data, the plot with the _____ (steeper/flatter) slope will represent a _____ (faster/slower) expansion rate, and will predict an age for the universe that is older.

7) On the blank graph in Figure 4 below, draw a Hubble plot for which the expansion rate of the universe is zero.

8) On the blank graph in Figure 5 below, draw a Hubble plot for which the expansion of the universe increases throughout the lifetime of the universe.

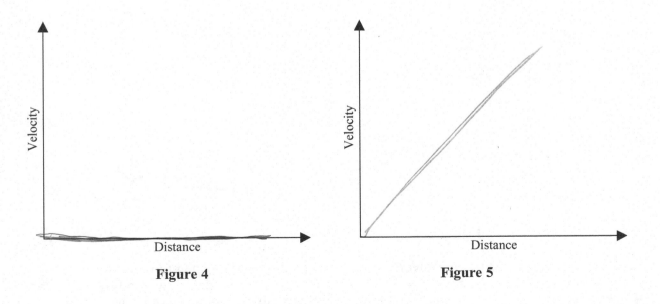

Figure 4   **Figure 5**

Part II: Our Universe

Recent observations indicate the Hubble plot for our universe actually looks more like the plot in Figure 6.

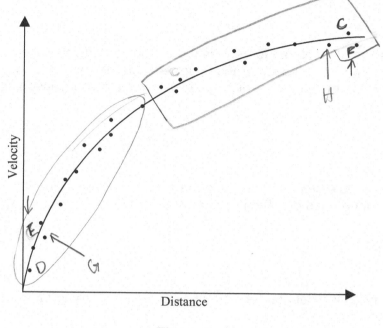

Figure 6

9) Parts a–h all refer to Figure 6. Draw or write the additional information on Figure 6 as instructed:

a) Draw a circle around the galaxies from which we receive light that was emitted closest to our present time.

b) Draw a square around the galaxies from which we receive light that was emitted furthest from our present time.

c) Write the letter C, and draw an arrow to the galaxies that are moving away from us with the fastest velocities.

d) Write the letter D, and draw an arrow to the galaxies that are moving away from us with the slowest velocities.

e) Write the letter E, and draw an arrow to the graph, where it has the steepest slope.

f) Write the letter F, and draw an arrow to the graph, where it has the flattest slope.

g) Write the letter G, and draw an arrow to the portion of the graph that corresponds to the fastest expansion rate.

h) Write the letter H, and draw an arrow to the portion of the graph that corresponds to the slowest expansion rate.

10) Based on the Hubble plot shown in Figure 6, would you say that the expansion rate of the universe is constant or (changing) with time? Explain your reasoning.

Diff areas relate to different extremes

11) Based on the Hubble plot in. Figure 6, is the expansion rate represented by the motion of galaxies far away from us faster than, (slower than), or the same as the expansion rate represented by the motions of nearby galaxies? Explain your reasoning.

flat slope

12) Based on the Hubble plot in Figure 6, is the expansion rate of the universe (increasing) or decreasing as time goes on? Explain your reasoning.

13) Consider the following debate between two students regarding their answer to the previous question:

Student 1: *The expansion rate of our universe must be slowing down as time goes on. If you look at the Hubble plot, you can see that the graph gets flatter. That means the farther away you look, the slower the expansion rate is. The rate at which the most distant galaxies are moving away from us has started to slow down and eventually the expansion rate of nearby galaxies will also slow down.*

Student 2: *I think you are reading the graph wrong. The slope of the graph tells you how fast the expansion rate of the universe is, not how fast a galaxy is moving. The farther we look into space, the further we are looking back in time. Since the slope of the Hubble plot is flatter in the past and steeper now, that means the expansion rate has sped up over time.*

Do you agree or disagree with either or both of the students? Explain your reasoning.

14) Based upon your previous answers, is the graph you drew in Question 8 correct or does it need to be redrawn? Explain your reasoning.

No   already knew

Part I: The Observable Universe

Each tiny dot in the picture below represents a galaxy. The Milky Way Galaxy is represented by a tiny dot at the center of the picture. All of the galaxies inside the circle can be seen from Earth. The circumference of this circle defines what is called our *observable universe*. Any galaxy that exists outside the circle is so far away that its light has not had time to reach Earth and is therefore not part of our observable universe.

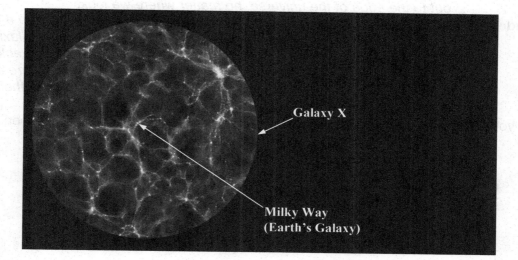

1) Do you think the galaxies we can see from Earth are the only galaxies in the *entire universe*? Explain your reasoning.

2) Draw a circle around Galaxy X that represents its *observable universe*.

3) Is the *observable universe* that you drew for Galaxy X different in size than the *observable universe* for Earth? Explain your reasoning.

4) Two students are talking about the *observable universe* for Galaxy X:

Student 1: *People living in Galaxy X have a strange view of the universe. When they look in one direction, they see a bunch of galaxies, but when they look in the other direction, all they see is empty space. Galaxy X must be at the edge of the universe since there's nothing but black, empty space beyond it. We're lucky we live at the center since we can see galaxies all the way out to the edge of the universe, no matter where we look.*

Student 2: *I think you're wrong. People living in Galaxy X would probably see a bunch of galaxies in every direction they look, but they can see some galaxies that we can't, just like we can see galaxies they can't. The observable universe for any galaxy should look similar to ours. I don't think we are at the center of the universe and I don't think Galaxy X is at the edge either.*

Do you agree or disagree with either or both of the students? Explain your reasoning.

Part II: An Analogy for Expansion

One way to try to understand and envision the expansion of the universe is by creating analogies that model the different aspects of our real expanding universe. One way to model the expanding universe is to use a "balloon" analogy. In this analogy, the space and time of the universe are modeled by the "surface" or "skin" of an expanding balloon. <u>The *entire universe* exists only on the surface of the balloon.</u> Light can travel only in the space and time along the surface of the balloon.

5) Do objects, light, or events in the *entire universe* also exist inside or outside of the balloon's surface in this analogy?

6) If you were to travel from galaxy to galaxy along the surface of the balloon, would you ever encounter an edge?

7) If you were to travel over the entire surface of the balloon universe, would you ever find a location that is the center of the *entire universe*?

8) Consider the following debate between two students about their answers to the previous questions:

Student 1:   *Someone living on the surface of this balloon universe will definitely encounter an edge and a center. All they have to do is look from their location across the inside of the balloon to a location on the other side. The center of the inside of the balloon is the center of the universe, and the far side would be the edge of what they could see. So there's definitely a center and an edge to the universe in the balloon analogy.*

Student 2:   *I think you misunderstand the analogy. The surface of the balloon is supposed to be the entire universe. The inside of the balloon isn't part of the universe and doesn't actually exist. You can't look through the inside of the balloon to the other side so there is no center in the middle or edge on the other side. In this analogy, people living in the balloon universe would never encounter a center or an edge.*

Do you agree or disagree with either or both of the students? Explain your reasoning.

9) The balloons on the previous page represent the universe at different times during its history. Draw an arrow underneath the balloons that points from the earliest time to the latest. Label the ends of the arrow with the words "earliest" and "latest."

10) Imagine you lived in a galaxy on the surface of the balloon. As the balloon expands, would all the other galaxies appear to move toward you or away from you?

11) Would your answers to the previous question be the same regardless of the galaxy in which you live, or would it change depending on the galaxy you inhabit?

12) In this analogy, do galaxies move relative to one another because they are traveling across the surface of the balloon, or do they move relative to one another because the balloon is expanding?

13) The balloon analogy is a helpful way to think about expansion, but no analogy is perfect. Some aspects of the real universe are captured by this analogy while others are not. The evidence we now have about the real universe implies the following statements (a–f) are all true. For each of these statements, state whether it is accurately captured by the balloon analogy or not, and explain your reasoning.

a) The real universe has no center.

b) The real universe has no edge.

c) The real universe is expanding.

d) The real universe is not round.

e) The real universe's expansion does not cause galaxies to change size.

f) The real universe is 4-dimensional (3 dimensions of space and 1 of time).

When the universe was 4 billion years old, Galaxy A was 3 billion light-years away from Galaxy B, as shown below. Imagine that the universe was not expanding, so the distance between Galaxy A and Galaxy B would not change over time.

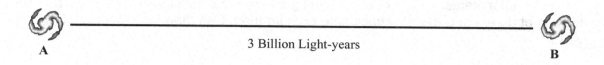

3 Billion Light-years

1) A star explodes in Galaxy B producing a large amount of light. How long will the light from this explosion take to reach Galaxy A?

2) How far did the light travel on its journey to Galaxy A?

3) How much older will the universe be by the time the light from the explosion reaches Galaxy A?

Because light takes time to travel from place to place in the universe, when we look at the night sky we are seeing stars and galaxies as they appeared in the past. For example, if we see a galaxy 1 million light-years away, we are seeing what the galaxy looked like 1 million years ago. We say this galaxy has a lookback time of 1 million years. Lookback time is the amount of time light takes to travel to us from a distant object.

4) When inhabitants of Galaxy A see the light from the explosion, what is the lookback time they associate with Galaxy B?

Our universe is expanding. This means the distance between galaxies is increasing. Imagine that Galaxy A and Galaxy B are in an expanding universe.

5) While the light from the explosion is traveling from Galaxy B to Galaxy A, does the distance between the two galaxies stay the same, become larger, or become smaller?

6) By the time the light from the explosion in Galaxy B reaches Galaxy A, is the distance between the galaxies more than, less than, or exactly 3 billion light-years?

7) By the time the light from the explosion in Galaxy B reaches Galaxy A, has more than, less than, or exactly 3 billion years elapsed since the star exploded?

8) By the time the light from the explosion in Galaxy B reaches Galaxy A, will the total distance traveled by the light be more than, less than, or exactly 3 billion light-years?

9) When the inhabitants of Galaxy A see the light from the explosion in Galaxy B, are they looking at an event with a lookback time of more than, less than, or exactly 3 billion years?

10) In the space below, provide a sketch that explains the reasoning behind your answers to Questions 5–9.

11) Consider the discussion between two students regarding their ideas about two distant galaxies in an expanding universe.

   Student 1: *Let's say light takes 5 billion years to travel from one galaxy to another. This means the two galaxies were separated by 5 billion light-years when the light began its journey.*

   Student 2: *If the light traveled for 5 billion years, then the distance between the two galaxies must have been less than 5 billion light-years when the light began its journey because the distances between galaxies are always increasing in the expanding universe.*

   Do you agree or disagree with either or both of the students? Explain your reasoning.

The figures below show three different Cases (1–3) in which light travels from Star S to Earth. The arrows represent light from Star S. The black box is covering up a region of spacetime through which light from Star S passes.

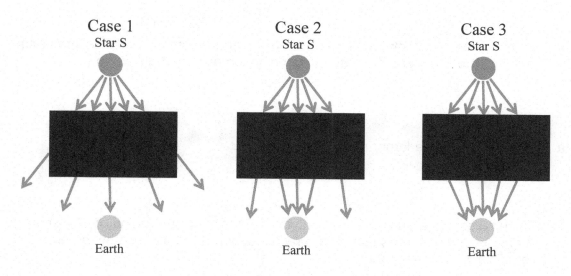

1) Rank the amount of light received by Earth from Star S, from greatest to least, for Cases 1–3.

In Cases 4–6 below, the black box has been removed and the region of spacetime that was covered is now shown.

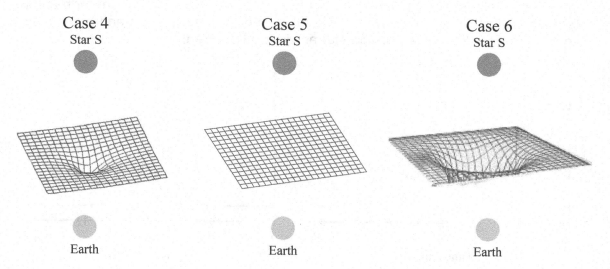

2) Match each of the Cases 4–6 with its corresponding situation in Cases 1–3. Explain your reasoning.

3) For Cases 4–6, rank the regions of spacetime based on the amount of mass present, from greatest to least. Explain your reasoning.

4) A high mass star and a low mass star are each warping regions of spacetime around themselves. The two stars move at the same speed as seen from Earth.

    a. Which star warps a larger region of spacetime?

    b. Which takes longer to move through your field of view: the region of spacetime warped by the low mass star, or the region of spacetime warped by the high mass star? Explain your reasoning.

5) Graphs A and B below show the brightness of a distant star as observed from Earth for a duration of time. The change in brightness of the distant star shown in Graph A is caused by Star X moving between Earth and the distant star. The change in brightness of the distant star shown in Graph B is caused by Star Y moving between Earth and the distant star. Stars X and Y move at the same speed. Assume Stars X and Y each follow the same path in front of the distant star as viewed from Earth.

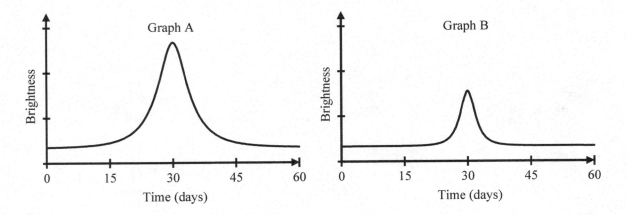

Use Graphs A and B to complete the sentence below using the words provided in parentheses ().

Star X warps spacetime _____ (more / less / equally) compared to Star Y because the mass of Star X is _____ (greater than / less than / the same as) the mass of Star Y. So Star X bends the light from the distant star _____ (more than/less than/the same as) Star Y. This means the brightness peak caused by Star X must be _____ (taller than / shorter than / the same as) the peak caused by Star Y. Also, because the mass of Star X is _____ (greater than / less than / the same as) the mass of Star Y, the region of spacetime it warps is _____ (larger / smaller / equal) in size. This means it takes a _____ (longer / shorter / equal) amount of time for the region of spacetime warped by Star X to move between Earth and Star S. So, the brightness peak caused by Star X will appear _____ (wider / narrower / the same width) on the graph compared to the peak caused by Star Y.

For the rest of this activity, we will assume that a star and the exoplanets that orbit that star will all follow the same path in front of the distant star. This means that a high-mass planet will create a peak in the distant star's light curve that is both taller and wider than the peak created by a low-mass planet.

In Figure 1 below, Planet P is orbiting Star Z. The figure shows Star Z and Planet P at five consecutive times as they move from left to right through the region of spacetime between a distant star and Earth.

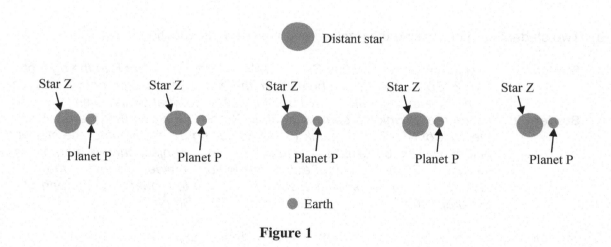

Figure 1

6) Which causes a greater warping of the region of spacetime around itself: Star Z or Planet P? Explain your reasoning.

7) Which moves between Earth and the distant star first: Star Z or Planet P?

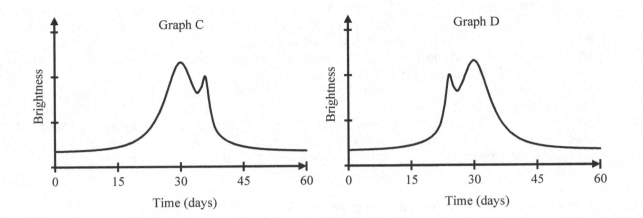

8) Which of the two Graphs (C or D) best corresponds to the observed brightness of the distant star depicted in Figure 1? Explain your reasoning.

9) Two students are discussing their answers to the previous question:

Student 1: *I think the correct graph is Graph C. We would see Planet P to the right of Star Z. So, the brightness bump from the planet needs to be on the right side of the brightness peak caused by Star Z. That is what Graph C shows.*

Student 2: *I disagree. I think the correct graph is Graph D. I agree that Planet P is to the right of Star Z, but I think you're confusing the positions of the star and planet with the corresponding times when each object causes a bump on the graph. Since the planet enters the region between Earth and the distant star first, we should see the bump due to Planet P on the part of the graph that's earlier in time. That matches Graph D.*

Do you agree or disagree with either or both of the students? Explain your reasoning.

10) Graphs E–H, below, show how the brightness of a distant star changes over time in different situations. In each situation, there is a star moving from left to right through the region of spacetime between Earth and the distant star. Each star that moves between the distant star and Earth is orbited by an exoplanet.

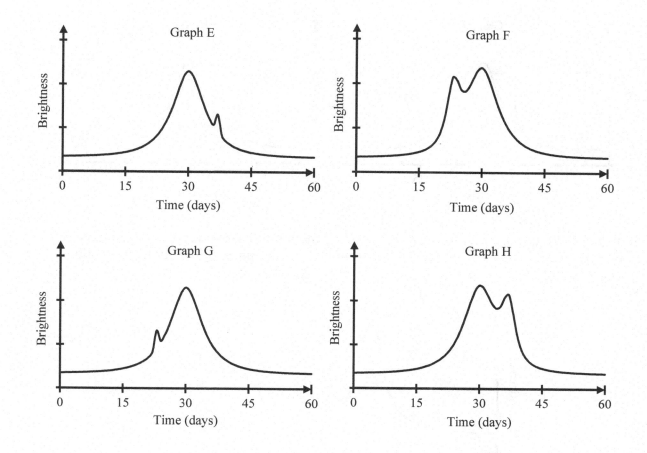

a. Which Graph (E–H) corresponds to the situation in which a star with a lower mass exoplanet located to the right of the star (as seen from Earth) moves through the region of spacetime between Earth and the distant star? Explain your reasoning.

b. Which Graph (E-H) corresponds to the situation in which a star with a higher mass exoplanet located to the left of the star (as seen from Earth) moves through the region of spacetime between Earth and the distant star? Explain your reasoning.

11) Graphs I and J, below, show how the brightness of a distant star changes over time in different situations. In each situation, there is a nearby star orbited by an exoplanet moving through the region of spacetime between Earth and the distant star. In which situation are the nearby star and its exoplanet farther apart as seen from Earth? Explain your reasoning.

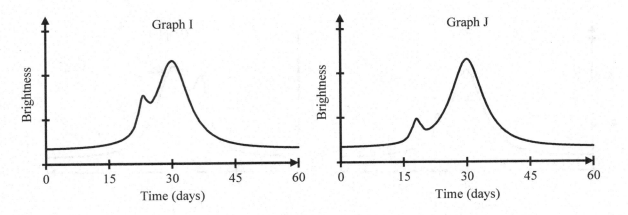

12) The graph below depicts the brightness of a distant star as observed from Earth. A nearby star moves from left to right as seen from Earth, passing between Earth and the distant star.

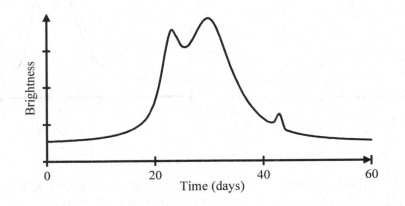

Sketch a picture of the extrasolar planet system moving between Earth and the distant star. Make sure to account for the sizes of the planets and their distances away from their parent star, as well as whether they are located to the left or right of their parent star.

Diagrams A and B below each represent a different way of thinking about how very large regions of the universe change over time. The dots in each diagram represent where matter exists in the universe.

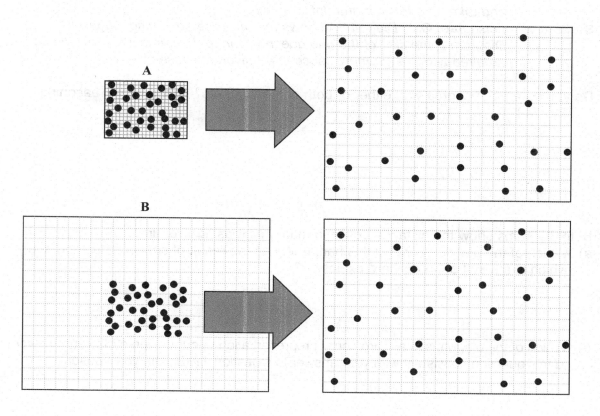

1) Which diagram, A or B, is a better representation of the universe we observe? Explain your reasoning.

2) In Diagram A, is the universe becoming bigger, smaller, or staying the same size over time?

3) In Diagram B, is the universe becoming bigger, smaller, or staying the same size over time?

4) Two students are debating their answers to Questions 2 and 3:

   Student 1:   *Both diagrams show the universe becoming bigger. In Diagram A, the grid has expanded and become larger. In Diagram B, matter has spread out and take up a greater amount of space.*

   Student 2:   *I disagree. Only Diagram A shows the universe becoming bigger. In Diagram B the size of the grid doesn't change. Matter is just moving into an already existing empty space in a universe whose size doesn't change.*

   Do you agree or disagree with either or both of the students? Explain your reasoning.

5) Both diagrams show the distance between matter increasing over time.
   a) Which of the diagrams shows this happening as the result of space expanding and which is a result of an outward explosion?

   b) Which of the diagrams is a more correct representation of our universe? Is your answer to this question consistent with your answer to Question 1? Explain your reasoning.

Consider the three diagrams (C, D, and E) shown below. These diagram each represent a single region of the universe, but at different times during the history of the universe.

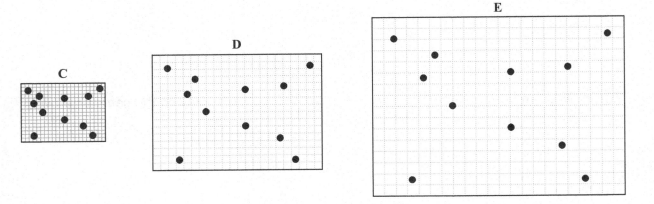

6) Draw an arrow below Diagrams C, D, and E. The arrow should point from the diagram that represents the earliest time in the universe's history to the diagram that represents the latest time in the universe's history. Label the ends of the arrow with the words "earliest" and "latest."

7) In which drawing does the region of space have:
   a) the highest matter density

   b) the greatest concentration of energy?

   c) the highest temperature?

   Explain your reasoning.

8) Imagine you could watch the history of the universe like a movie <u>playing backward</u>. The movie starts today and ends at the beginning of the universe. Describe what you would see for every region of the universe as the movie played and you looked further back in time. Your answer should discuss how regions of the universe change in terms of temperature, density, and size.

Your answers to the previous questions are all part of the *Big Bang theory*. The Big Bang theory describes the universe as starting 13.7 billion years ago and how it has changed over time.

9) Three students are discussing their understandings of the Big Bang theory:

Student 1: *I think I understand the Big Bang now. At the beginning, all the matter in the universe was compacted into a small, hot, dense ball. This ball of matter then exploded into empty space. When we look at the universe, we see galaxies moving away from us. The Big Bang model explains this, since all matter should be flying away from the center point of the explosion.*

Student 2: *I disagree. I think what the Big Bang theory is saying is that all the matter in the universe was once compacted into a really dense and hot object that expanded over time. But there wasn't an explosion of matter into empty space. Instead, the universe carried pieces of matter away from each other as it expanded in size.*

Student 3: *You're both wrong. I agree that the universe was once smaller in size and that pieces of matter have been carried away from each other by the expansion of the universe. But remember how we learned from Einstein's equation $E = mc^2$ that matter can be converted into energy and energy can be converted into matter? I think this means that if we go back to the beginning of the universe, it would be so incredibly small, dense and hot that matter itself couldn't exist. I bet at the very beginning, the universe would have been composed of pure energy with no matter there at all.*

Which students do you agree or disagree with? Explain your reasoning.

10) Based on your previous answers, complete the following sentences:

The Big Bang theory says that the universe started out with a/an _____ temperature and a/an _____ density. Originally, there was no _____, only pure _____. From this initial state, each region of the universe _____ in size. This caused its temperature and density to _____. When the temperature was cool enough, energy could transform into _____.

11) Look at Diagram A again. Next to Diagram A, make a drawing of what you think that region of the universe would have looked like at the very first instant it existed.